MW00875235

The Village Collector's Reader

HOOP

The Village Collector's Reader

Selections from the works of
Charles Dickens

LINDA ROSEWOOD HOOPER

1931-HOOP

Library of Congress Number: 00-191402

ISBN Softcover: 0-7388-2718-5

This book was printed in the United States of America.

To order additional copies of this book, contact:

Xlibris Corporation

1-888-7-XLIBRIS

www.Xlibris.com

Orders@Xlibris.com

Contents

-HOOP

1931-HOOP

Peggotty's Boat House. Frontispiece to David Copperfield.

Introduction

When I was a girl, my mother let me play with a decorative plate. The clever potter had carved and painted in relief thatched cot tage, a stone bridge over a boulder-filled creek, and a forest. With my little fingers I walked with the fairies who lived in the cottage, turned over the rocks to catch frogs, and crossed the bridge to climb the trees on the other side.

When I first held a Dickens' Village piece—it was The Old Curiosity Shop—my associations with it were much different from someone who might not be as familiar with the source that inspired it. The excitement of Dickens' Village collectors reminds me of that imaginary world of my childhood. Collectors must imagine what goes on inside their little ceramic houses!

I offer this book to Dickens' Village collectors who would like an introduction to the Dickens' world that I know. My hope is that your pleasure in your collection will be increased; and if you haven't already, perhaps you may even want to read his books yourself. Although it is true that they were written more than 150 years ago, I often meet people who remind me of his characters, or something occurs in my own life which I had already lived while reading his stories.

Although Dickens was interested in a great many subjects, he wasn't interested in architecture. Rarely is a building described from the outside, which not only gives Dickens' Village artists great latitude, it also gives me a great opportunity in making my selections. As I chose the passages for this anthology, I thought about all the associations a given cottage or shop or house might have, and found an appropriate scene to offer collectors. You may find that I didn't include your favorite. If so, it was either that I couldn't find any relevant passages ("Scotch Woolens") or because it is a kind of building, such as a church, which is rare in a Dickens novel, but popular in the Department 56 Dickens' Village.

You may worry that these excerpts won't make sense if you don't know the plot or characters. You needn't worry because Dickens is like no one else. G.K. Chesterton, who is the best Dickens critic, said it this way:

"As a general rule Dickens can be read in any order; not only in any order of books, but even in any order of chapters. In an average Dickens book every part is so amusing and alive that you can read parts backwards; you can read the quarrel first and then the cause of the quarrel; you can fall in love with a woman in the tenth chapter and then turn back to the first chapter to find out who she is."

Some people have said that Dickens books are long because he was "paid by the word." Actually, they are long because they were never meant to be read all at once. Dickens published his books serially, each section of the story appearing monthly or weekly. Each new installment–which was called a "number"–would appear on news stands and sell for only a shilling, a price affordable to many people, whereas an entire book was not. The long wait between installments was part of the enjoyment, just as people today enjoy serial stories in their television shows.

If you do pick up a Dickens novel, try to find an edition that indicates where each number begins and ends. Read one number at a time, and then try to put the book down for a week or a month. The rhythm of the story will soon capture you.

Linda Rosewood Hooper
Santa Cruz 1999

Works by Charles Dickens

Dickens wrote fourteen complete novels, between 1836 and 1870. His final novel was unfinished at his death. He wrote five "Christmas Books," including *A Christmas Carol,* and hundreds of short stories, newspaper articles, poems, speeches, and plays. My favorite of all is the Carol and it seems to be a favorite of Dickens' Village collectors too. It is one of the finest works of literature and although it is one of the most adapted, edited, and repackaged works in English, everyone should read it in its original text, at least once in life but better every year. *David Copperfield* seems to be the favorite of many, and *Pickwick Papers* is certainly the silliest. This anthology includes excerpts from a book of non-fiction, The *Uncommercial Traveller.* I also quoted from *A Child's History of England,* which isn't very accurate I'm told, but it has made me laugh out loud many times.

The Novels

The Posthumous Papers of the Pickwick Club

The Life and Adventures of Nicholas Nickleby

Barnaby Rudge: A Tale of the Riots of 'Eighty

The Adventures of Oliver Twist, or The Parish Boy's Progress

Old Curiosity Shop

The Life and Adventures of Martin Chuzzlewit, His Relatives, Friends, and Enemies

Dealings with the Firm of Dombey and Son

The Personal History, Adventures, Experiences, and Observation of David Copperfield the Younger

Little Dorrit

A Tale of Two Cities

Bleak House
Hard Times for These Times
Great Expectations
Our Mutual Friend
The Mystery of Edwin Drood(unfinished)

Ashbury Inn

A Christmas Carol, Stave Two

The holiday coach at the Ashbury Inn is crowded with merry folks enroute to Christmas parties, like these boys Scrooge recognizes during his visit with the Ghost of Christmas Past.

Good Heaven!" said Scrooge, clasping his hands together, as he looked about him. "I was bred in this place. I was a boy here!"

The Spirit gazed upon him mildly. Its gentle touch, though it had been light and instantaneous, appeared still present to the old man's sense of feeling. He was conscious of a thousand odours floating in the air, each one connected with a thousand thoughts, and hopes, and joys, and cares long, long, forgotten!

"Your lip is trembling," said the Ghost. "And what is that upon your cheek?"

Scrooge muttered, with an unusual catching in his voice, that it was a pimple; and begged the Ghost to lead him where he would.

"You recollect the way?" inquired the Spirit.

"Remember it!" cried Scrooge with fervour; "I could walk it blindfold."

"Strange to have forgotten it for so many years!" observed the Ghost. "Let us go on."

They walked along the road. Scrooge recognising every gate, and post, and tree; until a little market-town appeared in the distance, with its bridge, its church, and winding river. Some shaggy ponies now were seen trotting towards them with boys upon their backs, who called to other boys in country gigs and carts, driven by farmers. All these boys were in great spirits, and shouted to each other, until the broad fields were so full of merry music, that the crisp air laughed to hear it.

"These are but shadows of the things that have been," said the Ghost. "They have no consciousness of us."

The jocund travellers came on; and as they came, Scrooge knew and named them every one. Why was he rejoiced beyond all bounds to see them! Why did his cold eye glisten, and his heart leap up as they went past! Why was he filled with gladness when he heard them give each other Merry Christmas, as they parted at cross-roads and bye-ways, for their several homes! What was merry Christmas to Scrooge? Out upon merry Christmas! What good had it ever done to him?

"Coming Home from School" in *The Book of Christmas,* (1837), illustration by Robert Seymour.

Ashwick Lane Hose and Ladder

Oliver Twist, Chapter 48

Bill Sikes, driven mad after committing a horrible murder, wanders the slums of London until his attention is drawn by a fire—and firefighters.

And here he remained in such terror as none but he can know, trembling in every limb, and the cold sweat starting from every pore, when suddenly there arose upon the night-wind the noise of distant shouting, and the roar of voices mingled in alarm and wonder. Any sound of men in that lonely place, even though it conveyed a real cause of alarm, was something to him. He regained his strength and energy at the prospect of personal danger; and springing to his feet, rushed into the open air.

The broad sky seemed on fire. Rising into the air with showers of sparks, and rolling one above the other, were sheets of flame, lighting the atmosphere for miles round, and driving clouds of smoke in the direction where he stood. The shouts grew louder as new voices swelled the roar, and he could hear the cry of Fire! mingled with the ringing of an alarm-bell, the fall of heavy bodies, and the crackling of flames as they twined round some new obstacle, and shot aloft as though refreshed by food. The noise increased as he looked. There were people there–men and women–light, bustle. It was like new life to him. He darted onward–straight, headlong–dashing through brier and brake, and leaping gate and fence as madly as his dog, who careered with loud and sounding bark before him.

He came upon the spot. There were half-dressed figures tearing to and fro, some endeavouring to drag the frightened horses from the stables, others driving the cattle from the yard and out-houses, and others coming laden from the burning pile, amidst a shower of falling sparks, and the tumbling down of red-hot beams. The apertures, where doors and windows stood an hour ago, disclosed a mass of raging fire; walls rocked and crumbled into the burning well; the molten lead and iron poured down, white hot, upon the ground. Women and children shrieked, and men encouraged each other with noisy shouts and cheers. The clanking of the engine-pumps, and the spirting and hissing of the water as it fell upon the blazing wood, added to the tremendous roar. He shouted, too, till he was hoarse; and flying from memory and himself, plunged into the thickest of the throng.

Hither and thither he dived that night: now working at the pumps, and now hurrying through the smoke and flame, but never ceasing to engage himself wherever noise and men were thickest. Up and down the ladders, upon the roofs of buildings, over floors that quaked and trembled with his weight, under the lee of falling bricks and stones, in every part of that great fire was he; but he bore a charmed life, and had neither scratch nor bruise, nor weariness nor thought, till morning dawned again, and only smoke and blackened ruins remained.

This mad excitement over, there returned, with tenfold force, the dreadful consciousness of his crime. He looked suspiciously about him, for the men were conversing in groups, and he feared to be the subject of their talk. The dog obeyed the significant beck of his finger, and they drew off, stealthily, together. He passed near an engine where some men were seated, and they called to him to share in their refreshment. He took some bread and meat, and as he drank a draught of beer, heard the firemen, who were from London, talking about the murder. "He has gone to Birmingham, they say," said one: "but they'll have him yet, for the scouts are out, and by to-morrow night there'll be a cry all through the country."

He hurried off, and walked till he almost dropped upon the ground; then lay down in a lane, and had a long, but broken and uneasy sleep.

Barley Bree Farmhouse

Pickwick Papers, Chapter 7

M*r. Pickwick awakens after his first night at "Manor Farm, Dingley Dell."*

Pleasant, pleasant country," sighed the enthusiastic gentleman, as he opened his lattice window. "Who could live to gaze from day to day on bricks and slates, who had once felt the influence of a scene like this? Who could continue to exist, where there are no cows but the cows on the chimney-pots; nothing redolent of Pan but pan-tiles; no crop but stone crop? Who could bear to drag out a life in such a spot? Who I ask could endure it?" and, having cross-examined solitude after the most approved precedents, at considerable length Mr. Pickwick thrust his head out of the lattice, and looked around him.

The rich, sweet smell of the hayricks rose to his chamber window; the hundred perfumes of the little flower-garden beneath scented the air around; the deep-green meadow shone in the morning dew that glistened on every leaf as it trembled in the gentle air: and the birds sang as if every sparkling drop were a fountain of inspiration to them. Mr. Pickwick fell into an enchanting and delicious reverie.

Bean and Son Smithy Shop

Great Expectations, Chapter 12

Pip entertains the eccentric Miss Havisham with a blacksmith's song that Dickens had probably heard himself.

There was a song Joe used to hum fragments of at the forge, of which the burden was Old Clem. This was not a very ceremonious way of rendering homage to a patron saint; but I believe Old Clem stood in that relation towards smiths. It was a song that imitated the measure of beating upon iron, and was a mere lyrical excuse for the introduction of Old Clem's respected name. Thus, you were to hammer boys round—Old Clem! With a thump and a sound—Old Clem!

Beat it out, beat it out—Old Clem! With a clink for the stout—Old Clem! Blow the fire, blow the fire—Old Clem! Roaring dryer, soaring higher—Old Clem! One day soon after the appearance of the chair, Miss Havisham suddenly saying to me, with the impatient movement of her fingers, "There, there, there! Sing!" I was surprised into crooning this ditty as I pushed her over the floor. It happened so to catch her fancy that she took it up in a low brooding voice as if she were singing in her sleep. After that, it became customary with us to have it as we moved about, and Estella would often join in; though the whole strain was so subdued, even when there were three of us, that it made less noise in the grim old house than the lightest breath of wind.

Betsy Trotwood's Cottage

David Copperfield, Chapter 13

David Copperfield's Aunt Betsey is one of the finest women in literature. The first passage describes how David meets her; the second is a vivid description of her appearance and character. (Department 56 spells her name slightly different from Dickens' version.)

I followed the young woman, and we soon came to a very neat little cottage with cheerful bow-windows: in front of it, a small square gravelled court or garden full of flowers, carefully tended, and smelling deliciously.

"This is Miss Trotwood's," said the young woman. "Now you know; and that's all I have got to say." With which words she hurried into the house, as if to shake off the responsibility of my appearance; and left *me* standing at the garden-gate, looking disconsolately over the top of it towards the parlor-window, where a muslin curtain partly undrawn in the middle, a large round green screen or fan fastened on to the window-sill, a small table, and a great chair, suggested to me that my aunt might be at that moment seated in awful state.

My shoes were by this time in a woeful condition. The soles had shed themselves bit by bit, and the upper leathers had broken and burst until the very shape and form of shoes had departed from them. My hat (which had served me for a night-cap, too) was so crushed and bent, that no old battered handleless saucepan on a dunghill need have been ashamed to vie with it. My shirt and trousers, stained with heat, dew, grass, and the Kentish soil on which I had slept–and torn besides–might have frightened the birds from my aunt's garden, as I stood at the gate. My hair had known no comb or brush since I left London. My face, neck, and hands, from unaccustomed exposure to the air and sun, were burnt to a berry-brown. From head to foot I was powdered almost as white with chalk and dust, as if I had come out of a limekiln. In this plight, and with a strong consciousness of it, I waited to introduce myself to, and make my first impression on, my formidable aunt.

The unbroken stillness of the parlor-window leading me to infer, after awhile, that she was not there, I lifted up my eyes to the window above it, where I saw a florid, pleasant-looking gentleman, with a grey head, who shut up one eye in a grotesque manner, nodded his head at me several times, shook it at me as often, laughed, and went away.

I had been discomposed enough before; but I was so much the more discomposed by this unexpected behaviour, that I was on the point of slinking off, to think how I had best proceed, when there came out of the house a lady with her handkerchief tied over her cap, and a pair of gardening gloves on her hands, wearing a gardening pocket like a toll-man's apron, and carrying a great knife. I knew her immediately to be Miss Betsey, for she came stalking out of the house exactly as my poor mother had so often described her stalking up our garden at Blunderstone Rookery.

"Go away!" said Miss Betsey, shaking her head, and making a distant chop in the air with her knife. "Go along! No boys here!"

I watched her, with my heart at my lips, as she marched to a corner of her garden, and stooped to dig up some little root there. Then, without a scrap of courage, but with a great deal of desperation, I went softly in and stood beside her, touching her with my finger.

"If you please, ma'am," I began.

She started and looked up.

"If you please, aunt."

"EH?" exclaimed Miss Betsey, in a tone of amazement I have never heard approached.

"If you please, aunt, I am your nephew."

"Oh, Lord!" said my aunt. And sat flat down in the garden-path.

"I am David Copperfield, of Blunderstone, in Suffolk–where you came, on the night when I was born, and saw my dear mama. I have been very unhappy since she died. I have been slighted, and taught nothing, and thrown upon myself, and put to work not fit for me. It made me run away to you. I was robbed at first setting out, and have walked all the way, and have never slept in a bed since I began the journey." Here my self-support gave way all at once; and with a movement of my hands, intended to show her my ragged state, and call it to witness that I had suffered something, I broke into a passion of crying, which I suppose had been pent up within me all the week.

* * *

My aunt was a tall, hard-featured lady, but by no means ill-looking. There was an inflexibility in her face, in her voice, in her gait and carriage, amply sufficient to account for the effect she had made upon a gentle creature like my mother; but her features were rather handsome than otherwise, though unbending and austere. I particularly noticed she had a very quick, bright eye. Her hair, which was grey, was arranged in two plain divisions, under what I believe would be called a mob-cap; I mean a cap, much more common then than now, with side-pieces fastening under the chin. Her dress was of a lavender color, and perfectly neat; but scantily made, as if she desired to be as little encumbered as possible. I remember that I thought it, in form, more like a riding-habit with the superfluous skirt cut off, than anything else. She wore at her side a gentleman's gold watch, if I might judge from its size and make, with an appropriate chain and seals; she had some linen at her throat not unlike a shirt-collar, and things at her wrists like little shirt-wristbands.

Bishop's Oast House

The Uncommercial Traveller, "Boiled Beef of New England"

Dickens often writes of the joys of wine and the dangers of gin, but rarely of beer, which is made from the hops dried in the Bishop's Oast. However, in this essay Dickens faults a soup kitchen—referred to as The Depôt—for not serving beer with dinner.

Another drawback on the Whitechapel establishment, is the absence of beer. Regarded merely as a question of policy, it is very impolitic, as having a tendency to send the working men to the public-house, where gin is reported to be sold. But, there is a much higher ground on which this absence of beer is objectionable. It expresses distrust of the working man. It is a fragment of that old mantle of patronage in which so many estimable Thugs, so darkly wandering up and down the moral world, are sworn to muffle him. Good beer is a good thing for him, he says, and he likes it; the Depôt could give it him good, and he now gets it bad. Why does the Depôt not give it him good? Because he would get drunk. Why does the Depôt not let him have a pint with his dinner, which would not make him drunk? Because he might have had another pint, or another two pints, before he came. Now, this distrust is an affront, is exceedingly inconsistent with the confidence the managers express in their handbills, and is a timid stopping-short upon the straight highway. It is unjust and unreasonable, also. It is unjust, because it punishes the sober man for the vice of the drunken man. It is unreasonable, because any one at all experienced in such things knows that the drunken workman does not get drunk where he goes to eat and drink, but where he goes to drink–expressly to drink. To suppose that the working man cannot state this question to himself quite as plainly as I state it here, is to suppose that he is a baby, and is again to tell him in the old wearisome condescending patronising way that he must be goody-poody, and do as he is toldy-poldy, and not be a manny-panny or a voter-poter, but fold his handy-pandys, and be a childy-pildy.

Blenham Street Bank

A Christmas Carol, Stave Four

When Scrooge and the Last Spirit overhear this grotesque conversation, they are "on 'Change" and across the street from "The Bank" of England.

Lead on!'" said Scrooge. "Lead on! The night is waning fast, and it is precious time to me, I know. Lead on, Spirit!"

The Phantom moved away as it had come towards him. Scrooge followed in the shadow of its dress, which bore him up, he thought, and carried him along.

They scarcely seemed to enter the city; for the city rather seemed to spring up about them, and encompass them of its own act. But there they were, in the heart of it; on 'Change, amongst the merchants; who hurried up and down, and chinked the money in their pockets, and conversed in groups, and looked at their watches, and trifled thoughtfully with their great gold seals; and so forth, as Scrooge had seen them often.

The Spirit stopped beside one little knot of business men. Observing that the hand was pointed to them, Scrooge advanced to listen to their talk.

"No," said a great fat man with a monstrous chin. "I don't know much about it, either way. I only know he's dead."

"When did he die?" inquired another.

"Last night, I believe."

"Why, what was the matter with him?" asked a third, taking a vast quantity of snuff out of a very large snuff-box. "I thought he'd never die."

"God knows," said the first, with a yawn.

"What has he done with his money?" asked a red-faced gentleman with a pendulous excrescence on the end of his nose, that shook like the gills of a turkey-cock.

"I haven't heard," said the man with the large chin, yawning again. "Left it to his company, perhaps. He hasn't left it to me. That's all I know."

This pleasantry was received with a general laugh.

"It's likely to be a very cheap funeral," said the same speaker; "for upon my life I don't know of anybody to go to it. Suppose we make up a party and volunteer?"

"I don't mind going if a lunch is provided," observed the gentleman with the excrescence on his nose. "But I must be fed, if I make one."

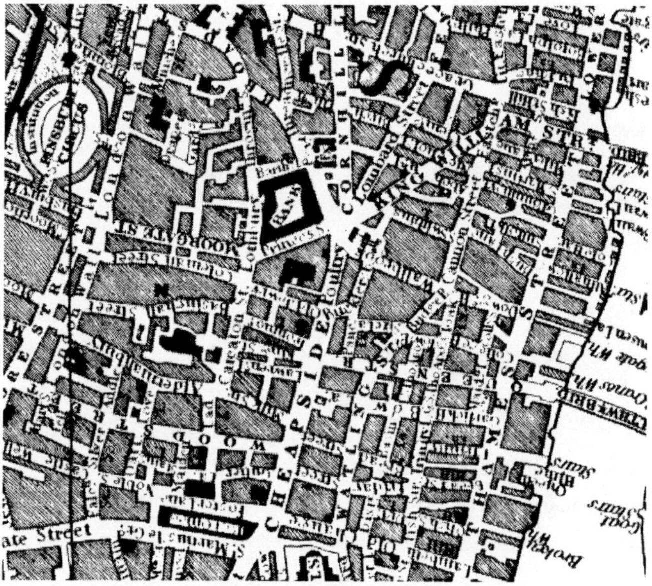

A map of the City of London, c. 1836,
showing the location of Bank of England.
The Exchange (marked "EX:) is on Cornhill Street,
just to the right of the Bank.

Boarding and Lodging School

David Copperfield, Chapter 7

Scrooge suffered in a boarding school, as we witness during his visit with the Ghost of Christmas Past. But he wasn't the only small boy to be sent away to school; David Copperfield was, and Dickens also.

School began in earnest next day. A profound impression was made upon me, I remember, by the roar of voices in the schoolroom suddenly becoming hushed as death when Mr. Creakle entered after breakfast, and stood in the doorway looking round upon us like a giant in a story-book surveying his captives.

Tungay stood at Mr. Creakle's elbow. He had no occasion, I thought, to cry out "Silence!" so ferociously, for the boys were all struck speechless and motionless.

Mr. Creakle was seen to speak, and Tungay was heard, to this effect.

"Now, boys, this is a new half. Take care what you're about, in this new half. Come fresh up to the lessons, I advise you, for I come fresh up to the punishment. I won't flinch. It will be of no use your rubbing yourselves; you won't rub the marks out that I shall give you. Now get to work, every boy!"

When this dreadful exordium was over, and Tungay had stumped out again, Mr. Creakle came to where I sat, and told me that if I were famous for biting, he was famous for biting, too. He then showed me the cane, and asked me what I thought of *that*, for a tooth? Was it a sharp tooth, hey? Was it a double tooth, hey? Had it a deep prong, hey? Did it bite, hey? Did it bite? At every question he gave me a fleshy cut with it that made me writhe; so I was very soon made free of Salem House (as Steerforth said), and very soon in tears also.

Not that I mean to say these were special marks of distinction which only I received. On the contrary, a large majority of the boys (especially the smaller ones) were visited with similar instances of notice, as Mr. Creakle made the round of the schoolroom. Half the establishment was writhing and crying, before the day's work began; and how much of it had writhed and cried before the day's work was over, I am really afraid to recollect, lest I should seem to exaggerate.

I should think there never can have been a man who enjoyed his profession more than Mr. Creakle did. He had a delight in cutting at the boys, which was like the satisfaction of a craving appetite. I am confident that he couldn't resist a chubby boy, especially; that there was a fascination in such a subject, which made him restless in his mind, until he had scored and marked him for the day. I was chubby myself, and ought to know. I am sure when I think of the fellow now, my blood rises against him with the disinterested indignation I should feel if I could have known all about him without having ever been in his power; but it rises hotly, because I know him to have been an incapable brute, who had no more right to be possessed of the great trust he held, than to be Lord High Admiral, or Commander-in-chief–in either of which capacities, it is probable, that he would have done infinitely less mischief.

Miserable little propitiators of a remorseless Idol, how abject we were to him! What a launch in life I think it now, on looking back, to be so mean and servile to a man of such parts and pretensions!

Here I sit at the desk again, watching his eye–humbly watching his eye, as he rules a ciphering book for another victim whose hands have just been flattened by that identical ruler, and who is trying to wipe the sting out with a pocket-handkerchief. I have plenty to do. I don't watch his eye in idleness, but because I am morbidly attracted to it, in a dread desire to know what he will do next, and whether it will be my turn to suffer, or somebody else's. A lane of small boys beyond me, with the same interest in his eye, watch it too. I think he knows it, though he pretends he don't. He makes dreadful mouths as he rules the ciphering book; and now he throws his eye sideways down our lane, and we all droop over our books and tremble. A moment afterwards we are again eyeing him. An unhappy culprit, found guilty of imperfect exercise, approaches at his command. The culprit falters excuses, and professes a determination to do better to-morrow. Mr. Creakle cuts a joke before he beats him, and we laugh at it,–miserable little dogs, we laugh, with our visages as white as ashes, and our hearts sinking into our boots.

Brick Abbey

Bleak House, Chapter 8

T*his scene of dawn as it reveals a ruined abbey is almost poetry.*

It was interesting when I dressed before daylight, to peep out of window, where my candles were reflected in the black panes like two beacons, and, finding all beyond still enshrouded in the indistinctness of last night, to watch how it turned out when the day came on. As the prospect gradually revealed itself, and disclosed the scene over which the wind had wandered in the dark, like my memory over my life, I had a pleasure in discovering the unknown objects that had been around me in my sleep. At first they were faintly discernible in the mist, and above them the later stars still glimmered. That pale interval over, the picture began to enlarge and fill up so fast, that, at every new peep, I could have found enough to look at for an hour. Imperceptibly, my candles became the only incongruous part of the morning, the dark places in my room all melted away, and the day shone bright upon a cheerful landscape, prominent in which the old Abbey Church, with its massive tower, threw a softer train of shadow on the view than seemed compatible with its rugged character. But so from rough outsides (I hope I have learnt), serene and gentle influences often proceed.

The ruins of Melrose Abbey, Scotland, destroyed during the Reformation.
Illustration from a history textbook published in 1874.

Brownlow House

Oliver Twist, Chapter 14

This passage regarding Mr. Brownlow's library contains self-referential jokes about the writing profession. Dickens was still new to his career when he wrote this.

Thus encouraged, Oliver tapped at the study door. On Mr. Brownlow calling to him to come in, he found himself in a little back room, quite full of books, with a window, looking into some pleasant little gardens. There was a table drawn up before the window, at which Mr. Brownlow was seated reading. When he saw Oliver, he pushed the book away from him, and told him to come near the table, and sit down. Oliver complied; marvelling where the people could be found to read such a great number of books as seemed to be written to make the world wiser. Which is still a marvel to more experienced people than Oliver Twist, every day of their lives.

"There are a good many books, are there not, my boy?" said Mr. Brownlow, observing the curiosity with which Oliver surveyed the shelves that reached from the floor to the ceiling.

"A great number, sir," replied Oliver. "I never saw so many."

"You shall read them, if you behave well," said the old gentleman kindly; "and you will like that, better than looking at the outsides,–that is, in some cases; because there *are* books of which the backs and covers are by far the best parts."

"I suppose they are those heavy ones, sir," said Oliver, pointing to some large quartos, with a good deal of gilding about the binding.

"Not always those," said the gentleman, patting Oliver on the head, and smiling as he did so; "there are other equally heavy ones, though of a much smaller size. How should you like to grow up a clever man, and write books, eh?"

"I think I would rather read them, sir," replied Oliver.

"What! wouldn't you like to be a book-writer?" said the old gentleman.

Oliver considered a little while; and at last said, he should think it would be a much better thing to be a book-seller; upon which the old gentleman laughed heartily, and declared he had said a very good thing. Which Oliver felt glad to have done, though he by no means knew what it was.

"Well, well," said the old gentleman, composing his features. "Don't be afraid! We won't make an author of you, while there's an honest trade to be learnt, or brick-making to turn to."

"Thank you, sir," said Oliver. At the earnest manner of his reply, the old gentleman laughed again; and said something about a curious instinct, which Oliver, not understanding, paid no very great attention to.

Mr. Brownlow is robbed of his handkerchief in *Oliver Twist*.
We know what kind of neighborhood this is because the building with the three balls hanging is a pawn shop.
Illustration by George Cruikshank.

Butter Tub Barn

Martin Chuzzlewit, Chapter 5

Dickens' stories are rarely set in the country, and he invented no barns worthy of mention. For the urban Dickens, a country farm was exotic. But he did know Farmer's Markets, when the country came to the city.

Mr. Pinch had a shrewd notion that Salisbury was a very desperate sort of place; an exceeding wild and dissipated city; and when he had put up the horse, and given the hostler to understand that he would look in again in the course of an hour or two to see him take his corn, he set forth on a stroll about the streets with a vague and not unpleasant idea that they teemed with all kinds of mystery and bedevilment. To one of his quiet habits this little delusion was greatly assisted by the circumstance of its being market-day, and the thoroughfares about the market-place being filled with carts, horses, donkeys, baskets, waggons, garden-stuff, meat, tripe, pies, poultry, and huckster's wares of every opposite description and possible variety of character. Then there were young farmers and old farmers, with smock-frocks, brown great-coats, drab great-coats, red worsted comforters, leather-leggings, wonderful shaped hats, hunting-whips, and rough sticks, standing about in groups, or talking noisily together on the tavern steps, or paying and receiving huge amounts of greasy wealth, with the assistance of such bulky pocket-books that when they were in their pockets it was apoplexy to get them out, and when they were out it was spasms to get them in again. Also there were farmers' wives in beaver bonnets and red cloaks, riding shaggy horses purged of all earthly passions, who went soberly into all manner of places without desiring to know why, and who, if required, would have stood stock still in a china-shop, with a complete dinner-service at each hoof. Also a great many dogs, who were strongly interested in the state of the market and the bargains of their masters; and a great confusion of tongues, both brute and human.

Candle Shop

David Copperfield, Chapter 46

Mr. Peggotty lights a candle of hope at the end of this poignant discussion regarding his niece, who has run away with a dishonorable man.

Mr. Peggotty," said I, taking the chair he handed me, "don't expect much! I have heard some news." "Of Em'ly!"

He put his hand, in a nervous manner, on his mouth, and turned pale, as he fixed his eyes on mine.

"It gives no clue to where she is; but she is not with him."

He sat down, looking intently at me, and listened in profound silence to all I had to tell. I well remember the sense of dignity, beauty even, with which the patient gravity of his face impressed me, when, having gradually removed his eyes from mine, he sat looking downward, leaning his forehead on his hand. He offered no interruption, but remained throughout perfectly still. He seemed to pursue her figure through the narrative, and to let every other shape go by him, as if it were nothing.

When I had done, he shaded his face, and continued silent. I looked out of the window for a little while, and occupied myself with the plants.

"How do you fare to feel about it, Mas'r Davy?" he inquired at length.

"I think that she is living," I replied.

"I doen't know. Maybe the first shock was too rough, and in the wildness of her art—! That there blue water as she used to speak on. Could she have thowt o' that so many year, because it was to be her grave!"

He said this, musing, in a low, frightened voice; and walked across the little room.

"And yet," he added, "Mas'r Davy, I have felt so sure as she was living–I have know'd, awake and sleeping, as it was so trew that I should find her–I have been so led on by it, and held up by it–that I doen't believe I can have been deceived. No! Em'ly's alive!"

He put his hand down firmly on the table, and set his sunburnt face into a resolute expression.

"My niece, Em'ly, is alive, sir!" he said, steadfastly. "I doen't know wheer it comes from, or how 'tis, but *I am told* as she's alive!"

He looked almost like a man inspired, as he said it. I waited for a few moments, until he could give me his undivided attention; and then proceeded to explain the precaution, that, it had occurred to me last night, it would be wise to take.

"Now, my dear friend–" I began.

"Thankee, thankee, kind sir," he said, grasping my hand in both of his.

"If she should make her way to London, which is likely–for where could she lose herself so readily as in this vast city; and what would she wish to do, but lose and hide herself, if she does not go home?–"

"And she won't go home," he interposed, shaking his head mournfully. "If she had left of her own accord, she might; not as 't was, sir."

"If she should come here," said I, "I believe there is one person, here, more likely to discover her than any other in the world. Do you remember–hear what I say, with fortitude–think of your great object!–do you remember Martha?'

"Of our town?"

I needed no other answer than his face.

"Do you know that she is in London?"

"I have seen her in the streets," he answered, with a shiver.

"But you don't know," said I, "that Emily was charitable to her, with Ham's help long before she fled from home. Nor, that, when we met one night, and spoke together in the room yonder, over the way, she listened at the door."

"Mas'r Davy!" he replied in astonishment. "That night when it snew so hard?"

"That night. I have never seen her since. I went back, after parting from you, to speak to her, but she was gone. I was unwilling to mention her to you then, and I am now; but she is the person of whom I speak, and with whom I think we should communicate. Do you understand?"

"Too well, sir," he replied. We had sunk our voices, almost to a whisper, and continued to speak in that tone.

"You say you have seen her. Do you think that you could find her? I could only hope to do so by chance."

"I think, Mas'r Davy, I know wheer to look."

"It is dark. Being together, shall we go out now, and try to find her to-night?"

He assented, and prepared to accompany me. Without appearing to observe what he was doing, I saw how carefully he adjusted the little room, put a candle ready and the means of lighting it, arranged the bed, and finally took out of a drawer one of her dresses (I remembered to have seen her wear it), neatly folded with some other garments, and a bonnet, which he placed upon a chair. He made no allusion to these clothes, neither did I. There they had been waiting for her, many and many a night, no doubt.

Chadbury Station and Train

Reprinted Pieces, "A Flight"

Dickens didn't like railroads. In only a few novels do characters travel by train. However, in this essay, Dickens gives us a clear picture of his almost child-like wonder and delight in speed.

The bell! With all my heart. It does not require *me* to do so much as even to flap my wings. Something snorts for me, something shrieks for me, something proclaims to everything else that it had better keep out of my way,–and away I go.

Ah! The fresh air is pleasant after the forcing-frame though it does blow over these interminable streets, and scatter the smoke of this vast wilderness of chimneys. Here we are–no, I mean there we were, for it has darted far into the rear–in Bermondsey where the tanners live. Flash! The distant shipping in the Thames is gone. Whirr! The little streets of new brick and red tile, with here and there a flagstaff growing like a tall weed out of the scarlet beans, and, everywhere, plenty of open sewer and ditch for the promotion of the public health, have been fired off in a volley. Whizz! Dust-heaps, market-gardens, and waste grounds. Rattle! New Cross Station. Shock! There we were at Croydon. Bur-r-r-r! The tunnel.

I wonder why it is that when I shut my eyes in a tunnel I begin to feel as if I were going at an Express pace the other way. I am clearly going back to London now; Compact Enchantress must have forgotten something, and reversed the engine. No! After long darkness, pale fitful streaks of light appear. I am still flying on for Folkstone. The streaks grow stronger–become continuous–become the ghost of day–become the living day–became I mean–the tunnel is miles and miles away, and here I fly through sunlight, all among the harvest and the Kentish hops.

There is a dreamy pleasure in this flying. I wonder where it was, and when it was, that we exploded, blew into space somehow, a Parliamentary Train, with a crowd of heads and faces looking at us out of cages, and some hats waving. Moneyed Interest says it was at Reigate Station. Expounds to Mystery how Reigate Station is so many miles from London, which Mystery again develops to Compact Enchantress. There might be neither a Reigate nor a London for me, as I fly away among the Kentish hops and harvest. What do *I* care?

Bang! We have let another Station off, and fly away regardless. Everything is flying. The hop gardens turn gracefully towards me, presenting regular avenues of hops in rapid flight, then whirl away. So do the pools and rushes, haystacks, sheep, clover in full bloom delicious to the sight and smell, corn-sheaves, cherry orchards, apple orchards, reapers, gleaners, hedges, gates, fields that taper off into little angular corners, cottages, gardens, now and then a church. Bang, Bang! A double-barrelled Station! Now a wood, now a bridge, now a landscape, now a cutting, now a–Bang! a single-barrelled Station–there was a cricket match somewhere with two white tents, and then four flying cows, then turnips–now the wires of the electric telegraph are all alive, and spin, and blurr their edges, and go up and down, and make the intervals between each other most irregular; contracting and expanding in the strangest manner. Now we slacken. With a screwing, and a grinding, and a smell of water thrown ashes, now we stop!

Chesterton Manor House

Bleak House, Chapter 6

Mr. Jarndyce, a lawyer, lives in a great country house, and perhaps the inside of Chesterton Manor resembles it. This passage from Bleak House *is one of the few in Dickens' works where architecture is described.*

It was one of those delightfully irregular houses where you go up and down steps out of one room into another, and where you come upon more rooms when you think you have seen all there are, and where there is a bountiful provision of little halls and passages, and where you find still older cottage-rooms in unexpected places, with lattice windows and green growth pressing through them. Mine, which we entered first, was of this kind, with an up-and-down roof, that had more corners in it than I ever counted afterwards, and a chimney (there was a wood-fire on the hearth) paved all around with pure white tiles, in every one of which a bright miniature of the fire was blazing. Out of this room, you went down two steps, into a charming little sitting-room, looking down upon a flower-garden, which room was henceforth to belong to Ada and me. Out of this you went up three steps, into Ada's bed-room, which had a fine broad window, commanding a beautiful view (we saw a great expanse of darkness lying underneath the stars), to which there was a hollow window-seat, in which, with a spring-lock, three dear Adas might have been lost at once. Out of this room, you passed into a little gallery, with which the other best rooms (only two) communicated, and so, by a little staircase of shallow steps, with a number of corner stairs in it, considering its length, down into the hall. But if, instead of going out at Ada's door, you came back into my room, and went out at the door by which you had entered it, and turned up a few crooked steps that branched off in an unexpected manner from the stairs, you lost yourself in passages, with mangles in them, and three-cornered tables, and a

Native-Hindoo chair, which was also a sofa, a box, and a bedstead, and looked in every form, something between a bamboo skeleton and a great bird-cage, and had been brought from India nobody knew by whom or when. From these, you came on Richard's room, which was part library, part sitting-room, part bed-room, and seemed indeed a comfortable compound of many rooms. Out of that, you went straight, with a little interval of passage, to the plain room where Mr. Jarndyce slept, all the year round, with his window open, his bedstead without any furniture standing in the middle of the floor for more air, and his cold-bath gaping for him in a smaller room adjoining. Out of that, you came into another passage, where there were back-stairs, and where you could hear the horses being rubbed down, outside the stable, and being told to Hold up, and Get over, as they slipped about very much on the uneven stones. Or you might, if you came out at another door (every room had at least two doors), go straight down to the hall again by half-a-dozen steps and a low archway, wondering how you got back there, or had ever got out of it.

Childe Pond and Skaters

Pickwick Papers, Chapter 30

Mr. Pickwick's friend Mr. Winkle professes to be "a sportsman"—or as we would say, a "jock." He decidedly is not. Yet he ventures out upon the ice anyway, and is eventually rescued by Mr. Pickwick. Mr. Pickwick is too dignified to skate—he slides.

Now," said Wardle, after a substantial lunch, with the agreeable items of strong-beer and cherry-brandy, had been done ample justice to; "what say you to an hour on the ice? We shall have plenty of time."

"Capital!" said Mr. Benjamin Allen.

"Prime!" ejaculated Mr. Bob Sawyer.

"You skate, of course, Winkle?" said Wardle.

"Ye-yes; oh, yes," replied Mr. Winkle. "I–I–am *rather* out of practice."

"Oh, *do* skate, Mr. Winkle," said Arabella. "I like to see it so much."

"Oh, it is *so* graceful," said another young lady.

A third young lady said it was elegant, and a fourth expressed her opinion that it was "swan-like."

"I should be very happy, I'm sure," said Mr. Winkle, reddening; "but I have no skates."

This objection was at once overruled. Trundle had a couple of pair, and the fat boy announced that there were half-a-dozen more down stairs: whereat Mr. Winkle expressed exquisite delight, and looked exquisitely uncomfortable.

Old Wardle led the way to a pretty large sheet of ice; and the fat boy and Mr. Weller, having shovelled and swept away the snow which had fallen on it during the night, Mr. Bob Sawyer adjusted his skates with a dexterity which to Mr. Winkle was perfectly marvellous, and described circles with his left leg, and cut figures of eight, and inscribed upon the ice, without once stopping for breath, a great many other pleasant and astonishing devices, to the excessive satisfaction of Mr. Pickwick, Mr. Tupman, and the ladies: which reached a pitch of positive enthusiasm, when old Wardle and Benjamin Allen, assisted by the aforesaid Bob Sawyer, performed some mystic evolutions, which they called a reel.

All this time, Mr. Winkle, with his face and hands blue with the cold, had been forcing a gimlet into the soles of his feet, and putting his skates on, with the points behind, and getting the straps into a very complicated and entangled state, with the assistance of Mr. Snodgrass, who knew rather less about skates than a Hindoo. At length, however, with the assistance of Mr. Weller, the unfortunate skates were firmly screwed and buckled on, and Mr. Winkle was raised to his feet.

"Now, then, sir," said Sam, in an encouraging tone; "off vith you, and show 'em how to do it."

"Stop, Sam, stop!" said Mr. Winkle, trembling violently, and clutching hold of Sam's arms with the grasp of a drowning man. "How slippery it is, Sam!"

"Not an uncommon thing upon ice, sir," replied Mr. Weller, "Hold up, sir!"

This last observation of Mr. Weller's bore reference to a demonstration Mr. Winkle made at the instant, of a frantic desire to throw his feet in the air, and dash the back of his head on the ice.

"These–these–are very ackward skates; ain't they, Sam?" inquired Mr. Winkle, staggering.

"I'm afeerd there's a orkard gen'l'm'n in 'em, sir," replied Sam.

"Now, Winkle," cried Mr. Pickwick, quite unconscious that there was anything the matter. "Come; the ladies are all anxiety."

"Yes, yes," replied Winkle, with a ghastly smile. "I'm coming."

"Just a goin' to begin," said Sam, endeavouring to disengage himself. "Now, sir, start off!

"'Stop an instant, Sam," gasped Mr. Winkle, clinging most affectionately to Mr. Weller. "I find I've got a couple of coats at home that I don't want, Sam. You may have them, Sam."

"Thank'ee, sir," replied Mr. Weller.

"Never mind touching your hat, Sam," said Mr. Winkle, hastily. "You needn't take your hand away to do that. I meant to have given you five shillings this morning for a Christmas-box, Sam. I'll give it you this afternoon, Sam."

"You're wery good, sir," replied Mr. Weller.

"Just hold me at first, Sam; will you?" said Mr. Winkle. "There–that's right. I shall soon get in th e way of it, Sam. Not too fast, Sam; not too fast."

Mr. Winkle stooping forward, with his body half doubled up, was being assisted over the ice by Mr. Weller, in a very singular and un-swan-like manner, when Mr. Pickwick most innocently shouted from the opposite bank:

"Sam!"

"Sir?

"Here. I want you."

"Let go, sir," said Sam. "Don't you hear the governor a callin'? Let go, sir."

With a violent effort, Mr. Weller disengaged himself from the grasp of the agonised Pickwickian, and, in so doing, administered a considerable impetus to the unhappy Mr. Winkle. With an accuracy which no degree of dexterity or practice could have insured, that unfortunate gentleman bore swiftly down into the centre of the reel, at the very moment when Mr. Bob Sawyer was performing a flourish of unparalleled beauty. Mr. Winkle struck wildly against him, and with a loud crash they both fell heavily down. Mr. Pickwick ran to the spot. Bob Sawyer had risen to his feet, but Mr. Winkle was far too wise to do anything of the kind, in skates. He was seated on the ice, making spasmodic efforts to smile; but anguish was depicted on every lineament of his countenance.

"Are you hurt?" inquired Mr. Benjamin Allen, with great anxiety.

"Not much," said Mr. Winkle, rubbing his back very hard. "I wish you'd let me bleed you," said Mr. Benjamin with great eagerness.

"No, thank you," replied Mr. Winkle hurriedly.

"I really think you had better," said Allen.

"Thank you," replied Mr. Winkle; "I'd rather not."

"What do *you* think, Mr. Pickwick?" inquired Bob Sawyer.

Mr. Pickwick was excited and indignant. He beckoned to Mr. Weller, and said in a stern voice, "Take his skates off."

"No; but really I had scarcely begun," remonstrated Mr. *Winkle.*

"Take his skates off," repeated Mr. Pickwick firmly.

The command was not to be resisted. Mr. Winkle allowed Sam to obey it in silence.

"Lift him up," said Mr. Pickwick. Sam assisted him to rise.

Mr. Pickwick retired a few paces apart from the by-standers; and, beckoning his friend to approach, fixed a searching look upon him, and uttered in a low, but distinct and emphatic tone, these remarkable words:

"You're a humbug, sir."

"A what?" said Mr. Winkle, starting.

"A humbug, sir. I will speak plainer, if you wish it. An impostor, sir."

With those words, Mr. Pickwick turned slowly on his heel, and rejoined his friends.

While Mr. Pickwick was delivering himself of the sentiment just recorded, Mr. Weller and the fat boy, having by their joint endeavours cut out a slide, were exercising themselves thereupon, in a very masterly and brilliant manner. Sam Weller, in particular, was displaying that beautiful feat of fancy-sliding which is currently denominated "knocking at the cobbler's door," and which is achieved by skimming over the ice on one foot, and occasionally giving a postman's knock upon it with the other. It was a good long slide, and there was something in the motion which Mr. Pickwick, who was very cold with standing still, could not help envying.

"It looks a nice warm exercise that, doesn't it?" he inquired of Wardle, when that gentleman was thoroughly out of breath, by reason of the indefatigable manner in which he had converted his legs into a pair of compasses, and drawn complicated problems on the ice.

"Ah, it does indeed," replied Wardle. "Do you slide?"

"I used to do so, on the gutters, when I was a boy," replied Mr. Pickwick.

"Try it now," said Wardle.

"Oh do please, Mr. Pickwick!" cried all the ladies.

"I should be very happy to afford you any amusement," replied Mr. Pickwick, "but I haven't done such a thing these thirty years."

"Pooh! pooh! Nonsense!" said Wardle, dragging off his skates with the impetuosity which characterised all his proceedings. "Here; I'll keep you company; come along!" And away went the good-tempered old fellow down the slide, with a rapidity which came very close upon Mr. Weller, and beat the fat boy all to nothing.

Mr. Pickwick paused, considered, pulled off his gloves and put them in his hat: took two or three short runs, baulked himself as often, and at last took another run, and went slowly and gravely down the slide, with his feet about a yard and a quarter apart, amidst the gratified shouts of all the spectators.

"Keep the pot a bilin', sir!" said Sam; and down went Wardle again, and then Mr. Pickwick, and then Sam, and then Mr. Winkle, and then Mr. Bob Sawyer, and then the fat boy, and then Mr. Snodgrass, following closely upon each other's heels, and running after each other with as much eagerness as if all their future prospects in life depended on their expedition.

Mr. Pickwick slides.

The Chop Shop

David Copperfield, Chapter 5

David Copperfield's cruel stepfather sends him away—alone—to a boarding school. He begins the trip with this lunch, which should have included chops.

The coach was in the yard, shining very much all over, but without any horses to it as yet; and it looked in that state as if nothing was more unlikely than its ever going to London. I was thinking this, and wondering what would ultimately become of my box, which Mr. Barkis had put down on the yard-pavement by the pole (he having driven up the yard to turn his cart), and also what would ultimately become of me, when a lady looked out of a bow-window where some fowls and joints of meat were hanging up, and said:

"Is that the little gentleman from Blunderstone?"

"Yes, ma'am," I said.

"What name?" inquired the lady.

"Copperfield, ma'am," I said.

"That won't do," returned the lady. "Nobody's dinner is paid for here, in that name."

"Is it Murdstone, ma'am?" I said.

"If you're Master Murdstone," said the lady, "why do you go and give another name, first?"

I explained to the lady how it was, who then rang a bell, and called out, "William! Show the coffee-room!" upon which a waiter came running out of a kitchen on the opposite side of the yard to show it, and seemed a good deal surprised when he was only to show it to me.

It was a large long room with some large maps in it. I doubt if I could have felt much stranger if the maps had been real foreign countries, and I cast away in the middle of them. I felt it was taking a liberty to sit down, with my cap in my hand, on the corner of the chair nearest the door; and when the waiter laid a cloth on purpose for me, and put a set of casters on it, I think I must have turned red all over with modesty.

He brought me some chops, and vegetables, and took the covers off in such a bouncing manner that I was afraid I must have given him some offence. But he greatly relieved my mind by putting a chair for me at the table, and saying very affably, "Now, six-foot! come on!"

I thanked him, and took my seat at the board; but found it extremely difficult to handle my knife and fork with anything like dexterity, or to avoid splashing myself with the gravy, while he was standing opposite, staring so hard, and making me blush in the most dreadful manner every time I caught his eye. After watching me into the second chop, he said:

"There's half a pint of ale for you. Will you have it now?"

I thanked him, and said, "Yes." Upon which he poured it out of a jug into a large tumbler, and held it up against the light, and made it look beautiful.

"My eye!" he said. "It seems a good deal, don't it?"

"It does seem a good deal," I answered with a smile. For it was quite delightful to me to find him so pleasant. He was a twinkling-eyed, pimple-faced man, with his hair standing upright all over his head; and as he stood with one arm a-kimbo, holding up the glass to the light with the other hand, he looked quite friendly.

"There was a gentleman here yesterday," he said–"a stout gentleman, by the name of Topsawyer–perhaps you know him?"

"No," I said, "I don't think–"

"In breeches and gaiters, broad-brimmed hat, grey coat, speckled choaker," said the waiter.

"No," I said bashfully, "I haven't the pleasure–"

"He came in here," said the waiter, looking at the light through the tumbler, "ordered a glass of this ale–*would* order it–I told him not–drank it, and fell dead. It was too old for him. It oughtn't to be drawn; that's the fact."

I was very much shocked to hear of this melancholy accident, and said I thought I had better have some water.

"Why you see," said the waiter, still looking at the light through the tumbler, with one of his eyes shut up, "our people don't like things being ordered and left. It offends 'em. But *I'll* drink it, if you like. I'm used to it, and use is everything. I don't think it'll hurt me, if I throw my head back, and take it off quick. Shall I?"

I replied that he would much oblige me by drinking it, if he thought he could do it safely, but by no means otherwise. When he did throw his head back, and take it off quick, I had a horrible fear, I confess, of seeing him meet the fate of the lamented Mr. Topsawyer, and fall lifeless on the carpet. But it didn't hurt him. On the contrary, I thought he seemed the fresher for it.

"What have we got here?" he said, putting a fork into my dish. "Not chops?"

"Chops," I said.

"Lord bless my soul!" he exclaimed, "I didn't know they were chops. Why, a chop's the very thing to take off the bad effects of that beer! Ain't it lucky?"

So he took a chop by the bone in one hand, and a potato in the other, and ate away with a very good appetite, to my extreme satisfaction. He afterwards took another chop, and another potato; and after that, another chop and another potato. When we had done, he brought me a pudding, and having set it before me, seemed to ruminate, and to become absent in his mind for some moments.

"How's the pie?" he said, rousing himself.

"It's a pudding," I made answer.

"Pudding!" he exclaimed. "Why, bless me, so it is! What!" looking at it nearer. "You don't mean to say it's a batter-pudding?"

"Yes, it is indeed."

"Why, a batter-pudding," he said, taking up a table-spoon, "is my favorite pudding! Ain't that lucky? Come on, little 'un, and let's see who'll get most."

The waiter certainly got most. He entreated me more than once to come in and win, but what with his table-spoon to my tea-spoon, his dispatch to my dispatch, and his appetite to my appetite, I was left far behind at the first mouthful, and had no chance with him. I never saw anyone enjoy a pudding so much, I think; and he laughed, when it was all gone, as if his enjoyment of it lasted still.

Cobles Police Station

Our Mutual Friend, Book iv, Chapter 40

In the Dickens world, criminals are much more common than police. But in **Our Mutual Friend**, *we find this small room, briefly visited by the principal characters. In this and other passages in the novel, Dickens likens the police station to a monastary.*

They alighted at last at the corner of a court, where there was a building with a bright lamp and a wicket gate. Its orderly appearance was very unlike that of the surrounding neighbourhood, and was explained by the inscription Police Station.

"We are not going in here, John?" said Bella, clinging to him.

"Yes, my dear; but of our own accord. We shall come out again as easily, never fear."

The whitewashed room was pure white as of old, the methodical book-keeping was in peaceful progress as of old, and some distant howler was banging against a cell-door as of old. The sanctuary was not a permanent abiding-place, but a kind of criminal Pickford's. The lower passions and vices were regularly ticked off in the books, warehoused in the cells, carted away as per accompanying invoice, and left little mark upon it.

Mr. Inspector placed two chairs for his visitors, before the fire, and communed in a low voice with a brother of his order (also of a half-pay and Royal Arms aspect), who, judged only by his occupation at the moment, might have been a writing-master setting copies. Their conference done, Mr. Inspector returned to the fireplace, and, having observed that he would step round to the Fellowships and see how matters stood, went out. He soon came back again, saying, "Nothing could be better, for they're at supper with Miss Abbey in the bar;" and then they all three went out together.

Cottage of Bob Cratchit and Tiny Tim

A Christmas Carol, Stave Three

This working-class house is said to be modeled on one of Dickens' child hood homes, the one in Camden Town, London.

They went on, invisible, as they had been before, into the suburbs of the town. It was remarkable quality of the Ghost (which Scrooge had observed at the baker's), that notwithstanding his gigantic size, he could accommodate himself to any place with ease; and that he stood beneath a low roof quite as gracefully and like a supernatural creature, as it was possible he could have done in any lofty hall.

And perhaps it was the pleasure the good Spirit had in showing off this power of his, or else it was his own kind, generous, hearty nature, and his sympathy with all poor men, that led him straight to Scrooge's clerk's; for there he went, and took Scrooge with him, holding to his robe; and on the threshhold of the door the Spirit smiled, and stopped to bless Bob Cratchit's dwelling with the sprinklings of his torch. Think of that! Bob had but fifteen "Bob" a-week himself; he pocketed on Saturdays but fifteen copies of his Christian name; and yet the Ghost of Christmas Present blessed his four-roomed house!

The house on Bayham street in Camden where Dickens's family lived.
Illustration by F. G. Kitton in *Dickens in Pen and Pencil.*

Counting House

Nicholas Nickleby, Chapter 25

The Department 56 Counting House belongs to Scrooge and Marley, but the place of business in this selection is from another novel. After many adventures, Nicholas falls in with the generous Cherryble Brothers, who offer him employment–in a merchants' counting house.

The old gentleman got out, with great alacrity, when they reached the Bank, and once more taking Nicholas by the arm, hurried him along Threadneedle Street, and through some lanes and passages on the right, until they, at length, emerged in a quiet shady little square. Into the oldest and cleanest-looking house of business in the square, he led the way. The only inscription on the door-post was "Cheeryble, Brothers;" but from a hasty glance at the directions of some packages which were lying about, Nicholas supposed that the Brothers Cheeryble were German-merchants.

Passing through a warehouse which presented every indication of a thriving business, Mr. Cheeryble (for such Nicholas supposed him to be, from the respect which had been shown him by the warehousemen and porters whom they passed) led him into a little partitioned-off counting-house like a large glass-case, in which counting-house there sat–as free from dust and blemish as if he had been fixed into the glass-case before the top was put on, and had never come out since–a fat, elderly, large-faced, clerk, with silver spectacles and a powdered head. department 56 Counting House belongs to Scrooge and Marley, but the novel. After many adventures, Nicholas falls in with the generous Cherryble Brothers, who offer him employment–in a merchants' counting house.

The old gentleman got out, with great alacrity, when they reached

Crowntree Inn

Pickwick Papers, Chapter 10

It is in a coaching inn that Mr. Pickwick meets one of Dickens' most beloved characters, Sam Weller.

There are in London several old inns, once the head-quarters of celebrated coaches in the days when coaches performed their journeys in a graver and more solemn manner than they do in these times; but which have now degenerated into little more than the abiding and booking places of country waggons. The reader would look in vain for any of these ancient hostelries, among the Golden Crosses and Bull and Mouths, which rear their stately fronts in the improved streets of London. If he would light upon any of these old places, he must direct his steps to the obscurer quarters of the town; and there in some secluded nooks he will find several, still standing with a kind of gloomy sturdiness, amidst the modern innovations which surround them.

In the Borough especially, there still remain some half dozen old inns, which have preserved their external features unchanged, and which have escaped alike the rage for public improvement, and the encroachments of private speculation. Great, rambling, queer, old places they are, with galleries, and passages, and staircases, wide enough and antiquated enough to furnish materials for a hundred ghost stories, supposing we should ever be reduced to the lamentable necessity of inventing any, and that the world should exist long enough to exhaust the innumerable veracious legends connected with old London Bridge, and its adjacent neighbourhood on the Surrey side.

It was in the yard of one of these inns–of no less celebrated a one than the White Hart–that a man was busily employed in brushing the dirt off a pair of boots, early on the morning succeeding the events narrated in the last chapter. He was habited in a coarse-striped waistcoat, with black calico sleeves, and blue glass buttons; drab breeches and leggings. A bright red handkerchief was wound in a very loose and unstudied style round his neck, and an old white hat was carelessly thrown on one side of his head. There were two rows of boots before him, one cleaned and the other dirty, and at every addition he made to the clean row, he paused from his work, and contemplated its results with evident satisfaction.

The yard presented none of that bustle and activity which are the usual characteristics of a large coach inn. Three or four lumbering waggons, with a pile of goods beneath its ample canopy, about the height of the second-floor window of an ordinary house, were stowed away beneath a lofty roof which extended over one end of the yard; and another, which was probably to commence its journey that morning, was drawn out into the open space. A double tier of bed-room galleries, with old clumsy balustrades, ran round two sides of the straggling area, and a double row of bells to correspond, sheltered from the weather by a little sloping roof, hung over the door leading to the bar and coffee-room. Two or three gigs and chaise-carts were wheeled up under different little sheds and pent-houses; and the occasional heavy tread of a cart-horse, or rattling of a chain at the further end of the yard, announced to anybody who cared about the matter, that the stable lay in that direction. When we add that a few boys in smock frocks were lying asleep on heavy packages, woolpacks, and other articles that were scattered about on heaps of straw, we have described as fully as need be the general appearance of the yard of the White Hart Inn, High Street, Borough, on the particular morning in question.

Sam Weller, of The White Hart Inn, meets the Pickwick Club.

Dover Coach

Pickwick Papers, Chapter 28

Although David Copperfield attempts to take the Dover coach to "make himself known to his aunt," he is cheated out of his fare, his baggage is stolen, and he walks all the way to Dover. So, in the interest of illustrating a coach that is actually conveying passengers, here is the "Muggleton Coach" as Mr. Pickwick and friends prepare for Christmas in the country.

We write these words now, many miles distant from the spot at which, year after year, we met on that day, a merry and joyous circle. Many of the hearts that throbbed so gaily then, have ceased to beat; many of the looks that shone so brightly then, have ceased to glow; the hands we grasped have grown cold; the eyes we sought, have hid their lustre in the grave; and yet the old house, the room, the merry voices and smiling faces, the jest, the laugh, the most minute and trivial circumstances connected with those happy meetings, crowd upon our mind at each recurrence of the season, as if the last assemblage had been but yesterday! Happy, happy Christmas, that can win us back to the delusions of our childish days; that can recall to the old man the pleasures of his youth; that can transport the sailor and the traveller, thousands of miles away, back to his own fire-side and his quiet home!

But we are so taken up and occupied with the good qualities of this saint Christmas, that we are keeping Mr. Pickwick and his friends waiting in the cold on the outside of the Muggleton coach, which they have just attained, well wrapped up in great-coats, shawls, and comforters. The portmanteaus and carpet-bags have been stowed away, and Mr. Weller and the guard are endeavouring to insinuate into the fore-boot a huge cod-fish several sizes too large for it–which is snugly packed up, in a long brown basket, with a layer of straw over the top, and which has been left to the last, in order that he may repose in safety on the half-dozen barrels of real native oysters, all the property of Mr. Pickwick, which have been arranged in regular order at the bottom of the receptacle. The interest displayed in Mr. Pickwick's countenance is most intense, as Mr. Weller and the guard try to squeeze the cod-fish into the boot, first head first, and then tail first, and then top upward, and then bottom upward, and then side-ways, and then long-ways, all of which artifices the implacable cod-fish sturdily resists, until the guard accidentally hits him in the very middle of the basket, whereupon be suddenly disappears into the boot, and with him, the head and shoulders of the guard himself, who, not calculating upon so sudden a cessation of the passive resistance of the cod-fish, experiences a very unexpected shock, to the unsmotherable delight of all the porters and bystanders. Upon this, Mr. Pickwick smiles with great good-humour, and drawing a shilling from his waistcoat pocket, begs the guard, as he picks himself out of the boot, to drink his health in a glass of hot brandy and water; at which the guard smiles too, and Messrs. Snodgrass, Winkle, and Tupman, all smile in company. The guard and Mr. Weller disappear for five minutes: most probably to get the hot brandy and water, for they smell very strongly of it, when they return, the coachman mounts to the box, Mr. Weller jumps up behind, the Pickwickians pull their coats round their legs and their shawls over their noses, the helpers pull the horse-cloths off, the coachman shouts out a cheery "All right," and away they go.

Fagin's Hide-A-Way

Oliver Twist, Chapter 8

One of the saddest observations about these scenes of London's nineteenth-century slums is that they can still be found in modern cities. The only thing to be said about Dickens' anti-Semitism in creating Fagin is that he had absorbed his cultural norms, and late in life realized how cruel stereotypes can be. The casual anti-Semitism in **Oliver Twist** *is as ugly a picture of London as its slums.*

Although Oliver had enough to occupy his attention in keeping sight of his leader, he could not help bestowing a few hasty glances on either side of the way, as he passed along. A dirtier or more wretched place he had never seen. The street was very narrow and muddy, and the air was impregnated with filthy odours. There were a good many small shops; but the only stock in trade appeared to be heaps of children, who, even at that time of night, were crawling in and out at the doors, or screaming from the inside. The sole places that seemed to prosper amid the general blight of the place, were the public-houses; and in them, the lowest orders of Irish were wrangling with might and main. Covered ways and yards, which here and there diverged from the main street, disclosed little knots of houses, where drunken men and women were positively wallowing in filth; and from several of the door-ways, great ill-looking fellows were cautiously emerging, bound, to all appearance, on no very well-disposed or harmless errands.

Oliver was just considering whether he hadn't better run away, when they reached the bottom of the hill. His conductor, catching him by the arm, pushed open the door of a house near Field Lane; and, drawing him into the passage, closed it behind them.

"Now, then!" cried a voice from below, in reply to a whistle from the Dodger.

"Plummy and slam!" was the reply.

This seemed to be some watchword or signal that all was right; for the light of a feeble candle gleamed on the wall at the remote end of the passage; and a man's face peeped out, from where a balustrade of the old kitchen staircase had been broken away.

"There's two on you," said the man, thrusting the candle farther out, and shading his eyes with his hand. "Who's the t' other one?"

"A new pal," replied Jack Dawkins, pulling Oliver forward.

"Where did he come from?"

"Greenland. Is Fagin up stairs?"

"Yes, he's a sortin' the wipes. Up with you!" The candle was drawn back, and the face disappeared.

Oliver, groping his way with one hand, and having the other firmly grasped by his companion, ascended with much difficulty the dark and broken stairs: which his conductor mounted with an ease and expedition that showed he was well acquainted with them. He threw open the door of a back-room, and drew Oliver in after him.

The walls and ceiling of the room were perfectly black with age and dirt. There was a deal table before the fire: upon which were a candle, stuck in a ginger-beer bottle, two or three pewter pots, a loaf and butter, and a plate. In a frying-pan, which was on the fire, and which was secured to the mantelshelf by a string, some sausages were cooking; and standing over them, with a toasting-fork in his hand, was a very old shrivelled Jew, whose villanous-looking and repulsive face was obscured by a quantity of matted red hair. He was dressed in a greasy flannel gown, with his throat bare; and seemed to be dividing his attention between the frying-pan and a clothes-horse, over which a great number of silk handkerchiefs were hanging. Several rough beds made of old sacks, were huddled side by side on the floor. Seated round the table were four or five boys, none older than the Dodger, smoking long clay pipes, and drinking spirits with the air of middle-aged men. These all crowded about their associate as he whispered a few words to the Jew; and then turned round and grinned at Oliver. So did the Jew himself, toasting-fork in hand.

"This is him, Fagin,' said Jack Dawkins; "my friend Oliver Twist."

Sir John Falstaff Inn

Pickwick Papers, Chapter 27

Here's another inn honoring an ancient lord, The Marquis of Granby. And it is the kind of inn that would satisfy Dickens as well as Sam Weller.

The Marquis of Granby in Mrs. Weller's time was quite a model of a road-side public-house of the better class–just large enough to be convenient, and small enough to be snug. On the opposite side of the road was a large sign-board on a high post, representing the head and shoulders of a gentleman with an apoplectic countenance, in a red coat with deep blue facings, and a touch of the same blue over his three-cornered hat, for a sky. Over that again were a pair of flags; beneath the last button of his coat were a couple of cannon; and the whole formed an expressive and undoubted likeness of the Marquis of Granby of glorious memory.

The bar window displayed a choice collection of geranium plants, and a well dusted row of spirit phials. The open shutters bore a variety of golden inscriptions, eulogistic of good beds and neat wines; and the choice group of countrymen and hostlers lounging about the stable-door and horse-trough, afforded presumptive proof of the excellent quality of the ale and spirits which were sold within. Sam Weller paused, when he dismounted from the coach, to note all these little indications of a thriving business, with the eye of an experienced traveller; and having done so, stepped in at once, highly satisfied with everything be had observed.

Fezziwig's Warehouse

A Christmas Carol, Stave Two

The Ghost of Christmas Past helps Scrooge remember this Christmas party hosted by his master, Mr. Fezziwig.

There were more dances, and there were forfeits, and more dances, and there was cake, and there was negus, and there was a great piece of Cold Roast, and there was a great piece of Cold Boiled, and there were mince-pies, and plenty of beer. But the great effect of the evening came after the Roast and Boiled, when the fiddler (an artful dog, mind! The sort of man who knew his business better than you or I could have told it him!) struck up "Sir Roger de Coverley." Then old Fezziwig stood out to dance with Mrs. Fezziwig. Top couple, too; with a good stiff piece of work cut out for them; three or four and twenty pair of partners; people who were not to be trifled with; people who *would* dance, and had no notion of walking.

But if they had been twice as many–ah, four times–old Fezziwig would have been a match for them, and so would Mrs. Fezziwig. As to *her*, she was worthy to be his partner in every sense of the term. If that's not high praise, tell me higher, and I'll use it. A positive light appeared to issue from Fezziwig's calves. They shone in every part of the dance like moons. You couldn't have predicted, at any given time, what would become of them next. And when old Fezziwig and Mrs. Fezziwig had gone all through the dance; advance and retire, both hands to your partner, bow and curtsey, corkscrew, thread-the-needle, and back again to your place; Fezziwig "cut"–cut so deftly, that he appeared to wink with his legs, and came upon his feet again without a stagger.

When the clock struck eleven, this domestic ball broke up. Mr. and Mrs. Fezziwig took their stations, one on either side of the door, and shaking hands with every person individually as he or she went out, wished him or her a Merry Christmas. When everybody had retired but the two 'prentices, they did the same to them; and thus the cheerful voices died away, and the lads were left to their beds; which were under a counter in the back-shop."

Flat of Ebenezer Scrooge (and Melancholy Tavern)

A Christmas Carol, Stave One

When Dickens did write of a particular building's appearance, it was often with fantastic anthropomorphism, as in the passage below.

Scrooge took his melancholy dinner in his usual melancholy tavern; and having read all the newspapers, and beguiled the rest of the evening with his banker's-book, went home to bed. He lived in chambers which had once belonged to his deceased partner. They were a gloomy suite of rooms, in a lowering pile of building up a yard, where it had so little business to be, that one could scarcely help fancying it must have run there when it was a young house, playing at hide-and-seek with other houses, and forgotten the way out again. It was old enough now, and dreary enough, for nobody lived in it but Scrooge, the other rooms being all let out as offices. The yard was so dark that even Scrooge, who knew its every stone, was fain to grope with his hands. The fog and frost so hung about the black old gateway of the house, that it seemed as if the Genius of the Weather sat in mournful meditation on the threshold.

C. Fletcher Public House

David Copperfield, Chapter II

After the death of his mother, David Copperfield is sent to work in a factory. He lodges with a poor family and fends for himself in London. His age? About twelve. It is entirely possible that this celebratory ale was drunk by young Dickens himself on a similar occasion.

We had half-an-hour, I think, for tea. When I had money enough, I used to get half-a-pint of ready-made coffee and a slice of bread and butter. When I had none, I used to look at a venison-shop in Fleet Street; or I have strolled, at such a time, as far as Covent Garden Market, and stared at the pine-apples. I was fond of wandering about the Adelphi, because it was a mysterious place, with those dark arches. I see myself emerging one evening from some of these arches, on a little public-house close to the river, with an open space before it, where some coal-heavers were dancing; to look at whom I sat down upon a bench. I wonder what they thought of me!

I was such a child, and so little, that frequently when I went into the bar of a strange public-house for a glass of ale or porter, to moisten what I had had for dinner, they were afraid to give it me. I remember one hot evening I went into the bar of a public-house, and said to the landlord:

"What is your best–your *very best*–ale a glass?" For it was a special occasion. I don't know what. It may have been my birth-day.

"Twopence-halfpenny," says the landlord, "is the price of the Genuine Stunning ale."

"Then," says I, producing the money, "just draw me a glass of the Genuine Stunning, if you please, with a good head to it."

The landlord looked at me in return over the bar, from head to foot, with a strange smile on his face; and instead of drawing the beer, looked round the screen and said something to his wife. She came out from behind it, with her work in her hand, and joined him in surveying me. Here we stand, all three, before me now. The landlord in his shirt sleeves, leaning against the bar window-frame; his wife looking over the little half-door; and I, in some confusion, looking up at them from outside the partition. They asked me a good many questions; as, what my name was, how old I was, where I lived, how I was employed, and how I came there. To all of which, that I might commit nobody, I invented, I am afraid, appropriate answers. They served me with the ale, though I suspect it was not the Genuine Stunning: and the landlord's wife, opening the little half-door of the bar, and bending down, gave me my money back, and gave me a kiss that was half admiring, and half compassionate, but all womanly and good, I am sure.

My Magnificent Order the at the Public House." *David Copperfield*

Gad's Hill Place

The Uncommercial Traveller, "Traveling Abroad"

Dickens begins an essay about visiting France with this curious scene where he meets a boy who hopes to someday live at Gad's Hill Place. This country house is Dickens' own home, in which he had wanted to live when a small boy.

Holloa!" said I, to the very queer small boy, "where do you live?"

"At Chatham," says he.

"What do you do there?" says I.

"I go to school," says he.

I took him up in a moment, and we went on. Presently, the very queer small boy says, "This is Gads-hill we are coming to, where Falstaff went out to rob those travellers, and ran away."

"You know something about Falstaff, eh?" said I.

"All about him," said the very queer small boy. "I am old (I am nine), and I read all sorts of books. But *do* let us stop at the top of the hill, and look at the house there, if you please!"

"You admire that house?" said I.

"Bless you, sir," said the very queer small boy, "when I was not more than half as old as nine, it used to be a treat for me to be brought to look at it. And now, I am nine, I come by myself to look at it. And ever since I can recollect, my father, seeing me so fond of it, has often said to me, 'If you were to be very persevering and were to work hard, you might some day come to live in it.' Though that's impossible!" said the very queer small boy, drawing a low breath, and now staring at the house out of window with all his might.

I was rather amazed to be told this by the very queer small boy; for that house happens to be *my* house, and I have reason to believe that what he said was true.

Golden Swan, White Horse, & Wrenbury Bakeries

A Christmas Carol, Stave Three

It was illegal for bakers to work on Sundays or Christmas. However, the ovens could not be allowed to cool, or else they would crack. So bakers sold the heat from the ovens to the poor, providing means for the sole hot meal in the week.

But soon the steeples called good people all, to church and chapel, and away they came, flocking through the streets in their best clothes, and with their gayest faces. And at the same time there emerged from scores of bye streets, lanes, and nameless turnings, innumerable people, carrying their dinners to the bakers' shops. The sight of these poor revellers appeared to interest the Spirit very much, for he stood with Scrooge beside him in a baker's doorway, and taking off the covers as their bearers passed, sprinkled incense on their dinners from his torch. And it was a very uncommon kind of torch, for once or twice when there were angry words between some dinner-carriers who had jostled each other, he shed a few drops of water on them from it, and their good humour was restored directly. For they said, it was a shame to quarrel upon Christmas Day. And so it was! God love it, so it was!

In time the bells ceased, and the bakers were shut up; and yet there was a genial shadowing forth of all these dinners and the progress of their cooking, in the thawed blotch of wet above each baker's oven; where the pavement smoked as if its stones were cooking too.

"Is there a peculiar flavour in what you sprinkle from your torch?" asked Scrooge.

"There is. My own."

"Would it apply to any kind of dinner on this day? "' asked Scrooge.

"To any kindly given. To a poor one most."'

The Grapes Inn

Our Mutual Friend, Book i, Chapter 6

Dickens describes an ideal public house so well that if you could find it, you would know it intimately.

The Six Jolly Fellowship-Porters, already mentioned as a tavern of a dropsical appearance, had long settled down into a state of hale infirmity. In its whole constitution it had not a straight floor, and hardly a straight line; but it had outlasted, and clearly would yet outlast, many a better-trimmed building, many a sprucer public-house. Externally, it was a narrow lopsided wooden jumble of corpulent windows heaped one upon another as you might heap as many toppling oranges, with a crazy wooden verandah impending over the water; indeed the whole house, inclusive of the complaining flag-staff on the roof, impended over the water, but seemed to have got into the condition of a faint-hearted diver who has paused so long on the brink that he will never go in at all.

This description applies to the river-frontage of the Six Jolly Fellowship-Porters. The back of the establishment, though the chief entrance was there, so contracted, that it merely represented in its connection with the front, the handle of a flat-iron set upright on its broadest end. This handle stood at the bottom of a wilderness of court and alley: which wilderness pressed so hard and close upon the Six Jolly Fellowship-Porters as to leave the hostelry not an inch of ground beyond its door. For this reason, in combination with the fact that the house was all but afloat at high water, when the Porters had a family wash the linen subjected to that operation might usually be seen drying on lines stretched across the reception-rooms and bed-chambers.

The wood forming the chimney-pieces, beams, partitions, floors, and doors, of the Six Jolly Fellowship-Porters, seemed in its old age fraught with confused memories of its youth. In many places it had become gnarled and riven, according to the manner of old trees; knots started out of it; and here and there it seemed to twist itself into some likeness of boughs. In this state of second childhood, it had an air of being in its own way garrulous about its early life. Not without reason was it often asserted by the regular frequenters of the Porters, that when the light shone full upon the grain of certain panels, and particularly upon an old corner cupboard of walnut-wood in the bar, you might trace little forests there, and tiny trees like the parent tree, in full umbrageous leaf.

The bar of the Six Jolly Fellowship-Porters was a bar to soften the human breast. The available space in it was not much larger than a hackney-coach; but no one could have wished the bar bigger, that space was so girt in by corpulent little casks, and by cordial-bottles radiant with fictitious grapes in bunches, and by lemons in nets, and by biscuits in baskets, and by the polite beer-pulls that made low bows when customers were served with beer, and by the cheese in a snug corner, and by the landlady's own small table in a snugger corner near the fire, with the cloth everlastingly laid. This haven was divided from the rough world by a glass partition and a half-door with a leaden sill upon it for the convenience of resting your liquor; but, over this half-door the bar's snugness so gushed forth, that, albeit customers drank there standing, in a dark and draughty passage where they were shouldered by other customers passing in and out, they always appeared to drink under an enchanting delusion that they were in the bar itself.

For the rest, both the tap and parlour of the Six Jolly Fellowship-Porters gave upon the river, and had red curtains matching the noses of the regular customers, and were provided with comfortable fireside tin utensils, like models of sugar-loaf hats, made in that shape that they might, with their pointed ends, seek out for themselves glowing nooks in the depths of the red coals, when they mulled your ale, or heated for you those delectable drinks, Purl, Flip, and Dog's Nose. The first of these humming compounds was a specialty of the Porters, which, through an inscription on its door-posts, gently appealed to your feelings as, "The Early Purl House." For, it would seem that Purl must always be taken early; though whether for any more distinctly stomachic reason than that, as the early bird catches the worm, so the early purl catches the customer, cannot here be resolved. It only remains to add that in the handle of the flat-iron, and opposite the bar, was a very little room like a three-cornered hat, into which no direct ray of sun, moon, or star, ever penetrated, but which was superstitiously regarded as a sanctuary replete with comfort and retirement by gaslight, and on the door of which was therefore painted its alluring name: Cosy.

Green Gate Cottage

Little Dorrit, Chapter 28

Arthur Clennam is staying at a friend's cottage in the country. Being a city man, the beauty of the countryside touches him deeply.

A tranquil summer sunset shone upon him as he approached the end of his walk, and passed through the meadows by the riverside. He had that sense of peace, and of being lightened of a weight of care, which country quiet awakens in the breasts of dwellers in towns. Everything within his view was lovely and placid. The rich foliage of the trees, the luxuriant grass diversified with wild flowers, the little green islands in the river, the beds of rushes, the water-lilies floating on the surface of the stream, the distant voices in boats borne towards him on the ripple of the water and the evening air, were all expressive of rest. In the occasional leap of a fish, or dip of an oar, or twittering of a bird not yet at roost, or distant barking of a dog, or lowing of a cow–in all such sounds, there was the prevailing breath of rest, which seemed to encompass him in every scent that sweetened the fragrant air. The long lines of red and gold in the sky, and the glorious track of the descending sun, were all divinely calm. Upon the purple tree-tops far away, and on the green height near at hand up which the shades were slowly creeping, there was an equal hush. Between the real landscape and its shadow in the water, there was no division; both were so untroubled and clear, and, while so fraught with solemn mystery of life and death, so hopefully reassuring to the gazer's soothed heart, because so tenderly and mercifully beautiful.

Clennam had stopped, not for the first time by many times, to look about him and suffer what he saw to sink into his soul, as the shadows, looked at, seemed to sink deeper and deeper into the water.

Green Grocer, Mermaid Fish shoppe, T. Wells Fruit and Spice, Abel Beesley Butcher

A Christmas Carol, Stave Three

N*owhere in Dickens are grocers and other food sellers more lovingly celebrated than here, Christmas Eve, in Christmas present.*

For the people who were shovelling away on the house-tops were jovial and full of glee; calling out to one another from the parapets, and now and then exchanging a facetious snowball–better-natured missile far than many a wordy jest–laughing heartily if it went right, and not less heartily if it went wrong. The poulterers' shops were still half open, and the fruiterers' were radiant in their glory. There were great, round, pot-bellied baskets of chestnuts, shaped like the waistcoats of jolly old gentlemen, lolling at the doors, and tumbling out into the street in their apoplectic opulence. There were ruddy, brown-faced, broad-girthed Spanish Onions, shining in the fatness of their growth like Spanish Friars, and winking from their shelves in wanton slyness at the girls as they went by, and glanced demurely at the hung-up mistletoe. There were pears and apples, clustered high in blooming pyramids; there were bunches of grapes, made, in the shopkeepers' benevolence, to dangle from conspicuous hooks, that people's mouths might water gratis as they passed; there were piles of filberts, mossy and brown, recalling, in their fragrance, ancient walks among the woods, and pleasant shufflings, ankle deep through withered leaves; there were Norfolk Biffins, squab and swarthy, setting off the yellow of the oranges and lemons, and, in the great compactness of their juicy persons, urgently entreating and beseeching to be carried home in paper bags and eaten after dinner. The very gold and silver fish, set forth among these choice fruits in a bowl, though members of a dull and stagnant-blooded race, appeared to know that there was something going on; and, to a fish, went gasping round and round their little world in slow and passionless excitement.

The Grocers'! oh the Grocers'! nearly closed, with perhaps two shutters down, or one; but through those gaps such glimpses! It was not alone that the scales descending on the counter made a merry sound, or that the twine and roller parted company so briskly, or that the canisters were rattled up and down like juggling tricks, or even that the blended scents of tea and coffee were so grateful to the nose, or even that the raisins were so plentiful and rare, the almonds so extremely white, the sticks of cinnamon so long and straight, the other spices so delicious, the candied fruits so caked and spotted with molten sugar as to make the coldest lookers-on feel faint and subsequently bilious. Nor was it that the figs were moist and pulpy, or that the French plums blushed in modest tartness from their highly-decorated boxes, or that everything was good to eat and in its Christmas dress; but the customers were all so hurried and so eager in the hopeful promise of the day, that they tumbled up against each other at the door, crashing their wicker baskets wildly, and left their purchases upon the counter, and came running back to fetch them, and committed hundreds of the like mistakes in the best humour possible; while the Grocer and his people were so frank and fresh that the polished hearts with which they fastened their aprons behind might have been their own, worn outside for general inspection, and for Christmas daws to peck at if they chose.

"Market–Christmas Eve" in *The Book of Christmas* (1837), illustrated by Robert Seymour

Hembleton Pewterer (and Sweep)

Oliver Twist, Chapter 3

One hopes the chimney sweep sharing a building with the pewterer is **not** *the kind of sweep Oliver meets.*

This here boy, sir, wot the parish wants to 'prentis," said Mr. Gamfield

"Ay, my man," said the gentleman in the white waistcoat, with a condescending smile. "What of him?"

"If the parish vould like him to learn a light pleasant trade, in a good 'spectable chimbley-sweepin' bisness," said Mr. Gamfield, "I wants a 'prentis, and I am ready to take him."

"Walk in," said the gentleman in the white waistcoat. Mr. Gamfield having lingered behind, to give the donkey another blow on the head, and another wrench of the jaw, as a caution not to run away in his absence, followed the gentleman with the white waistcoat into the room where Oliver had first seen him.

"It's a nasty trade," said Mr. Limbkins, when Gamfield had again stated his wish.

"Young boys have been smothered in chimneys before now," said another gentleman.

"That's acause they damped the straw afore they lit it in the chimbley to make 'em come down agin," said Gamfield; "that's all smoke, and no blaze; vereas smoke ain't o' no use at all in making a boy come down, for it only sinds him to sleep, and that's wot he likes. Boys is wery obstinit, and wery lazy, gen'lmen, and there's nothink like a good hot blaze to make 'em come down vith a run. It's humane too, gen'lmen, acause, even if they've stuck in the chimbley, roasting their feet makes 'em struggle to hextricate theirselves."

The gentleman in the white waistcoat appeared very much amused by this explanation; but his mirth was speedily checked by a look from Mr. Limbkins. The board then proceeded to converse among themselves for a few minutes, but in so low a tone, that the words "saving of expenditure," "looked well in the accounts," "have a printed report published," were alone audible. These only chanced to be heard, indeed, on account of their being very frequently repeated with great emphasis.

At length the whispering ceased; and the members of the board, having resumed their seats and their solemnity, Mr. Limbkins said:

"We have considered your proposition, and we don't approve of it."

"Not at all," said the gentleman in the white waistcoat.

"Decidedly not," added the other members.

As Mr. Gamfield did happen to labour under the slight imputation of having bruised three or four boys to death already, it occurred to him that the board had, perhaps, in some unaccountable freak, taken it into their heads that this extraneous circumstance ought to influence their proceedings. It was very unlike their general mode of doing business, if they had; but still, as he had no particular wish to revive the rumour, he twisted his cap in his hands, and walked slowly from the table.

"So you won't let me have him, gen'lmen?" said Mr. Gamfield, pausing near the door.

"No," replied Mr. Limbkins; "at least, as it's a nasty business, we think you ought to take something less than the premium we offered."

Mr. Gamfield's countenance brightened, as, with a quick step, he returned to the table, and said,

"What'll you give, gen'lmen? Come! Don't be too hard on a poor man. What'll you give?"

"I should say, three pound ten was plenty," said Mr. Limbkins.

"Ten shillings too much," said the gentleman in the white waistcoat.

"Come!" said Gamfield; "say four pound, gen'lmen. Say four pound, and you've got rid on him for good and all. There!"

"Three pound ten," repeated Mr. Limbkins, firmly.

"Come! I'll split the difference, gen'lmen," urged Gamfield. "Three pound fifteen."

"Not a farthing more," was the firm reply of Mr. Limbkins. "You're desperate hard upon me, gen'lmen," said Gamfield, wavering.

"Pooh! pooh! nonsense!" said the gentleman in the white waistcoat. "He'd be cheap with nothing at all, as a premium. Take him, you silly fellow! He's just the boy for you. He wants the stick, now and then: it'll do him good; and his board needn't come very expensive, for he hasn't been over-fed since he was born. Ha! ha! ha!"

Mr. Gamfield gave an arch look at the faces round the table, and, observing a smile on all of them, gradually broke into a smile himself. The bargain was made. Mr. Bumble was at once instructed that Oliver Twist and his indentures were to be conveyed before the magistrate, for signature and approval, that very afternoon.

Ivy Glen Church

David Copperfield, Chapter 2

Dickens rarely mentions churches except as a place where couples go to be married. Young David Copperfield, however, gives us this charming picture of a church in the country.

Here is our pew in the church. What a high-backed pew! With a window near it, out of which our house can be seen, and *is* seen many times during the morning's service, by Peggotty, who likes to make herself as sure as she can that it's not being robbed, or is not in flames. But though Peggotty's eye wanders, she is much offended if mine does, and frowns to me, as I stand upon the seat, that I am to look at the clergyman. But I can't always look at him–I know him without that white thing on, and I am afraid of his wondering why I stare so, and perhaps stopping the service to inquire–and what am I to do? It's a dreadful thing to gape, but I must do something. I look at my mother, but *she* pretends not to see me. I look at a boy in the aisle, and *he* makes faces at me. I look at the sunlight coming in at the open door through the porch, and there I see a stray sheep–I don't mean a sinner, but mutton–half making up his mind to come into the church. I feel that if I looked at him any longer, I might be tempted to say something out loud; and what would become of me then! I look up at the monumental tablets on the wall, and try to think of Mr. Bodgers late of this parish, and what the feelings of Mrs. Bodgers must have been, when affliction sore, long time Mr. Bodgers bore, and physicians were in vain. I wonder whether they called in Mr. Chillip, and he was in vain; and if so, how he likes to be reminded of it once a week. I look from Mr. Chillip, in his Sunday neckcloth, to the pulpit; and think what a good place it would be to play in, and what a castle it would make, with another boy coming up the stairs to attack it, and having the velvet cushion with the tassels thrown down on his head. In time my eyes gradually shut up; and, from seeming to hear the clergyman singing a drowsy song in the heat, I hear nothing, until I fall off the seat with a crash, and am taken out, more dead than alive, by Peggotty.

Thomas Kersey Coffeehouse

The Uncommercial Traveller, "Refreshments for Travellers"

The traveller who hopes for a quick dinner is the victim of bad food and worse service in this hilarious scene that shows us that Victorian "fast food" was not so different from our own. Who hasn't decided against the "snack bar" and tried an airport restaurant, only to be treated something like this?

You are going off by railway, from any Terminus. You have twenty minutes for dinner, before you go. You want your dinner, and like Dr. Johnson, Sir, you like to dine. You present to your mind, a picture of the refreshment-table at that terminus. The conventional shabby evening-party supper–accepted as the model for all termini and all refreshment stations, because it is the last repast known to this state of existence of which any human creature would partake, but in the direst extremity–sickens your contemplation, and your words are these: I cannot dine on stale sponge-cakes that turn to sand in the mouth. I cannot dine on shining brown patties, composed of unknown animals within, and offering to my view the device of an indigestible star-fish in leaden pie-crust without. I cannot dine on a sandwich that has long been pining under an exhausted receiver. I cannot dine on barley-sugar. I cannot dine on Toffee." You repair to the nearest hotel, and arrive, agitated in the coffee-room.

It is a most astonishing fact that the waiter is very cold to you. Account for it how you may, smooth it over how you will, you cannot deny that he is cold to you. He is not glad to see you, he does not want you, he would much rather you hadn't come. He opposes to your flushed condition, an immovable composure. As if this were not enough, another waiter, born, as it would seem, expressly to look at you in this passage of your life, stands at a little distance, with his napkin under his arm and his hands folded, looking at you with all his might. You impress on your waiter that you have ten minutes for dinner, and he proposes that you shall begin with a bit of fish which will be ready in twenty. That proposal declined, he suggests–as neat originality–"a weal or mutton cutlet." You close with either cutlet, any cutlet, anything. He goes, leisurely, behind a door and calls down some unseen shaft. A ventriloquial dialogue ensues, tending finally to the effect that weal only, is available on the spur of the moment. You anxiously call out, "Veal, then!" Your waiter having settled that point, returns to array your tablecloth, with a table napkin folded cocked-hat-wise (slowly, for something out of window engages his eye), a white wine-glass, a green wine-glass, a blue finger-glass, a tumbler, and a powerful field battery of fourteen casters with nothing in them; or at all events–which is enough for your purpose–with nothing in them that will come out. All this time, the other waiter looks at you–with an air of mental comparison and curiosity, now, as if it had occurred to him that you are rather like his brother. Half your time gone, and nothing come but the jug of ale and the bread, you implore your waiter to "See after that cutlet, waiter; pray do!" He cannot go at once, for he is carrying in seventeen pounds of American cheese for you to finish with, and a small Landed Estate of celery and water-cresses. The other waiter changes his leg, and takes a new view of you, doubtfully, now, as if he had rejected the resemblance to his brother, and had begun to think you more like his aunt or his grandmother. Again you beseech your waiter with pathetic indignation, to "see after that cutlet!" He steps out to see after it, and by-and-by, when you are going away without it, comes back with it. Even then, he will not take the sham silver cover off, without a pause for a flourish, and a look at the musty cutlet as if he were surprised to see it–which cannot possibly be the case, he must have seen it so often before. A sort of fur has been produced upon its surface by the cook's art, and in a sham silver vessel staggering on two feet instead of three, is a cutaneous kind of sauce, of brown pimples and pickled cucumber. You order the bill, but your waiter cannot bring your bill yet, because he is bringing, instead, three flinty-hearted potatoes and two grim head of broccoli, like the occasional ornaments on area railings, badly boiled. You know that you will never come to this pass, any more than to the cheese and celery, and you imperatively demand your bill; but, it takes time to get, even when gone for, because your waiter has to communicate with a lady who lives behind a sash-window in a corner, and who appears to have to refer to several Ledgers before she can make it out–as if you had been staying there a year. You become distracted to get away, and the other waiter, once more changing his leg, still looks at you–but suspiciously, now, as if you had begun to remind him of the party who took the great-coats last winter. Your bill at last brought and paid, at the rate of sixpence a mouthful, your waiter reproachfully reminds you that "attendance is not charged for a single meal," and you have to search in all your pockets for sixpence more. He has a worse opinion of you than ever, when you have given it to him, and lets you out into the street with the air of one saying to himself, as you cannot doubt he is, "I hope we shall never see *you* here again!"

Kensington Palace

A Child's History of England, Chapter 23

The only Dickens work in which palaces play a significant part is **A Child's History of England**, *a hilarious if inaccurate trip through battles, betrayals, and beheadings. This passage is representative of Dickens' opinion of those who inhabit such fine houses.*

King Edward the Fourth was not quite twenty-one years of age when he took that unquiet seat upon the throne of England. The Lancaster party, the Red Roses, were then assembling in great numbers near York, and it was necessary to give them battle instantly. But the stout Earl of Warwick, leading for the young king, and the young king himself closely following him, and the English people crowding round the royal standard, the White and the Red Roses met, on a wild March day, when the snow was falling heavily, at Towton; and there such a furious battle raged between them, that the total loss amounted to forty thousand men,–all Englishmen, fighting, upon English ground, against one another. The young king gained the day, took down the heads of his father and brother from the walls of York, and put up the heads of some of the most famous noblemen engaged in the battle on the other side. Then he went to London, and was crowned with great splendor.

A new parliament met. No fewer than one hundred and fifty of the principal noblemen and gentlemen on the Lancaster side were declared traitors; and the king, who had very little humanity, though he was handsome in person, and agreeable in manners, resolved to do all he could to pluck up the Red Rose, root and branch.

Queen Margaret, however, was still active for her young son. She obtained help from Scotland and from Normandy, and took several important English castles. But Warwick soon retook them; the queen lost all her treasure on board ship in a great storm; and both she and her son suffered great misfortunes.

Once, in the winter weather, as they were riding through a forest, they were attacked and plundered by a party of robbers; and when they had escaped from these men, and were passing alone and on foot through a thick, dark part of the wood, they came all at once, upon another robber. So the queen, with a stout heart, took the little prince by the hand, and going straight up to that robber, said to him, " My friend, this is the young son of your lawful king! I confide him to your care." The robber was surprised, but took the boy in his arms, and faithfully restored him and his mother to their friends. In the end, the queen's soldiers being beaten and dispersed, she went abroad again, and kept quiet for the present.

Now, all this time, the deposed King Henry was concealed by a Welsh knight, who kept him close in his castle. But next year the Lancaster party, recovering their spirits, raised a large body of men, and called him out of his retirement to put him at their head. They were joined by some powerful noblemen who had sworn fidelity to the new king, but who were ready, as usual, to break their oaths whenever they thought there was anything to be got by it. One of the worst things in the history of the war of the Red and White Roses is the ease with which these noblemen, who should have set an example of honor to the people, left either side as they took slight offence, or were disappointed in their greedy expectations, and joined the other.

King's Road Post Office

Pickwick Papers, Chapter 33

Sam Weller reads a valentine aloud to his father that he has composed and is about to post. If the dialect confuses, just try reading it out loud.

Sam dipped his pen into the ink to be ready for any corrections, and began with a very theatrical air:

" 'Lovely–.' "

"Stop," said Mr. Weller, ringing the bell. "A double glass o' the inwariable, my dear."

"Very well, sir," replied the girl; who with great quickness appeared, vanished, returned, and disappeared.

"They seem to know your ways here," observed Sam.

"Yes," replied his father, "I've been here before, in my time. Go on, Sammy."

" 'Lovely creetur,' " repeated Sam.

" 'Tain't in poetry, is it?" interposed his father.

"No, no," replied Sam.

"Werry glad to hear it," said Mr. Weller. "Poetry's unnat'ral; no man ever talked poetry 'cept a beadle on boxin' day, or Warren's blackin', or Rowland's oil, or some o' them low fellows; never you let yourself down to talk poetry, my boy. Begin agin, Sammy."

Mr. Weller resumed his pipe with critical solemnity, and Sam once more commenced, and read as follows.

" 'Lovely creetur i feel myself a dammed'–."

"That ain't proper," said Mr. Weller, taking his pipe from his mouth.

"No; it ain't 'dammed'," observed Sam, holding the letter up to the light, "it's 'shamed,' there's a blot there–'I feel myself ashamed.' "

"Werry good," said Mr. Weller. "Go on."

" ' Feel myself ashamed, and completely cir–' I forget what this here word is," said Sam, scratching his head with the pen, in vain attempts to remember.

"Why don't you look at it, then?" inquired Mr. Weller.

"So I *am* a lookin' at it," replied Sam, "but there's another blot. Here's a 'c,' and a 'i,' and a 'd.' "

" Circumwented, p'haps," suggested Mr. Weller.

"No, it ain't that," said Sam, "circumscribed; that's it."

"That ain't as good a word as circumwented, Sammy," said Mr. Weller, gravely.

"Think not?" said Sam.

"Nothin' like it," replied his father.

"But don't you think it means more?" inquired Sam.

"Vell p'raps it is a more tenderer word," said Mr. Weller, after a few moments' reflection. "Go on, Sammy."

" 'Feel myself ashamed and completely circumscribed in a dressin' of you, for you *are* a nice gal and nothin' but it.' "

"That's a werry pretty sentiment," said the elder Mr. Weller, removing his pipe to make way for the remark.

"Yes, I think it is rayther good," observed Sam, highly flattered.

"Wot I like in that 'ere style of writin'," said the elder Mr. Weller, "is that there ain't no callin' names in it,–no Wenuses, nor nothin' o' that kind. Wot's the good o' callin' a young 'ooman a Wenus or a angel, Sammy?"

"Ah! what, indeed?" replied Sam.

"You might jist as well call her a griffin, or a unicorn, or a king's arms at once, which is werry well known to be a collection o' fabulous animals," added Mr. Weller.

"Just as well," replied Sam.

"Drive on, Sammy," said Mr. Weller.

Sam complied with the request, and proceeded as follows; his father continuing to smoke, with a mixed expression of wisdom and complacency, which was particularly edifying.

" 'Afore I see you, I thought all women was alike.' "

"So they are," observed the elder Mr. Weller, parenthetically.

" 'But now,' " continued Sam, " 'now I find what a reg'lar soft-headed, inkred'lous turnip I must ha' been; for there ain't nobody like you, though *I* like you better than nothin' at all.' I thought it best to make that rayther strong," said Sam, looking up.

Mr. Weller nodded approvingly, and Sam resumed.

" 'So I take the privilidge of the day, Mary, my dear–as the gen'l'm'n in difficulties did, ven he valked out of a Sunday–to tell you that the first and only time I see you, your likeness was took on my hart in much quicker time and brighter colours than ever a likeness was took by the profeel macheen (wich p'raps you may have heerd on Mary my dear) altho it *does* finish a portrait and put the frame and glass on complete, with a hook at the end to hang it up by, and all in two minutes and a quarter.' "

"I am afeerd that werges on the poetical, Sammy," said Mr. Weller, dubiously.

"No it don't," replied Sam, reading on very quickly, to avoid contesting the point:

" 'Except of me Mary my dear as your walentine and think over what I've said.–My dear Mary I will now conclude.' That's all," said Sam.

"That's rather a sudden pull up, ain't it, Sammy?" inquired Mr. Weller.

"Not a bit on it," said Sam; "she'll vish there wos more, and that's the great art o' letter writin."

J. Lytes Coal Merchant

The Battle of Life, Part Two

In one of Dickens' less-known Christmas books, he personified a coal fire as the guest of a Christmas party.

Now the music struck up, and the dance commenced. The bright fire crackled and sparkled, rose and fell, as though it joined the dance itself, in right good fellowship. Sometimes, it roared as if it would make music too. Sometimes it flashed and beamed as if it were the eye of the old room: it winked too, sometimes, like a knowing patriarch, upon the youthful whisperers in corners. Sometimes, it sported with the holly-boughs; and, shining on the leaves by fits and starts, made them look as if they were in the cold winter night again, and fluttering in the wind. Sometimes its genial humour grew obstreperous, and passed all bounds; and then it cast into the room, among the twinkling feet, with a loud burst, a shower of harmless little sparks, and in its exultation leaped and bounded, like a mad thing, up the broad old chimney.

Maylie Cottage

Oliver Twist, Chapter 29

One cannot remember the Maylie Cottage without feeling the sweetness of Rose Maylie. It is, after all the art and science of architecture is done, the people who make a house a home.

In a handsome room: though its furniture had rather the air of old-fashioned comfort, than of modern elegance: there sat two ladies at a well-spread breakfast-table. Mr. Giles, dressed with scrupulous care in a full suit of black, was in attendance upon them. He had taken his station some half-way between the sideboard and the breakfast-table; and, with his body drawn up to its full height, his head thrown back, and inclined the merest trifle on one side, his left leg advanced, and his right hand thrust into his waistcoat, while his left hung down by his side, grasping a waiter, looked like one who laboured under a very agreeable sense of his own merits and importance.

Of the two ladies, one was well advanced in years; but the high-backed oaken chair in which she sat, was not more upright than she. Dressed with the utmost nicety a precision, in a quaint mixture of by-gone costume, with some slight concessions to the prevailing taste, which rather served to point the old style pleasantly than to impair its effect, she sat, in a stately manner, with her hands folded on the table before her. Her eyes (and age had dimmed but little of brightness) were attentively fixed upon her young companion.

The younger lady was in the lovely bloom and spring-time of womanhood; at that age, when, if ever angels be for God's good purposes enthroned in mortal forms, they may be, without impiety, supposed to abide in such as hers.

She was not past seventeen. Cast in so slight and exquisite a mould; so mild and gentle; so pure and beautiful; that earth seemed not her element, nor its rough creatures her fit companions. The very intelligence that shone in her deep blue eye, and was stamped upon her noble head, seemed scarcely of her age, or of the world; and yet the changing expression of sweetness and good

humour, the thousand lights that played about the face, and left no shadow there; above all, the smile, the cheerful, happy smile, were made for Home, and fireside peace and happiness.

Mulberrie Court Brownstones

David Copperfield, Chapter 24

When David Copperfield come of age, his aunt rents for him a small apartment in London. He invites some other young men over for his first dinner party, with hired servants and a hired meal. The chapter from which this is excerpted is entitled "My First Dissipation."

One of Steerforth's friends was named Grainger, and the other Markham. They were both very gay and lively fellows; Grainger, something older than Steerforth; Markham, youthful-looking, and I should say not more than twenty. I observed that the latter always spoke of himself indefinitely, as "a man," and seldom or never in the first person singular.

"A man might get on very well here, Mr. Copperfield," said Markham–meaning himself.

"It's not a bad situation," said I, "and the rooms are really commodious."

"I hope you have both brought appetites with you?" said Steerforth.

"Upon my honor," returned Markham, "town seems to sharpen a man's appetite. A man is hungry all day long. A man is perpetually eating."

Being a little embarrassed at first, and feeling much too young to preside, I made Steerforth take the head of the table when dinner was announced, and seated myself opposite to him. Everything was very good; we did not spare the wine; and he exerted himself so brilliantly to make the thing pass off well, that there was no pause in our festivity. I was not quite such good company during dinner as I could have wished to be, for my chair was opposite the door, and my attention was distracted by observing that the handy young man went out of the room very often, and that his shadow always presented itself, immediately afterwards, on the wall of the entry, with a bottle at its mouth. The "young gal" likewise occasioned me some uneasiness: not so much by neglecting to wash the plates, as by breaking them. For being of an inquisitive disposition, and unable to confine herself (as her positive instructions were) to the pantry, she was constantly peering in at us, and constantly imagining herself detected; in which belief, she several times retired upon the plates (with which she had carefully paved the floor), and did a great deal of destruction.

These, however, were small drawbacks, and easily forgotten when the cloth was cleared, and the dessert put on the table; at which period of the entertainment the handy young man was discovered to be speechless. Giving him private directions to seek the society of Mrs. Crupp, and to remove the "young gal" to the basement also, I abandoned myself to enjoyment.

I began, by being singularly cheerful and light-hearted; all sorts of half-forgotten things to talk about, came rushing into my mind, and made me hold forth in a most unwonted manner. I laughed heartily at my own jokes, and everybody else's; called Steerforth to order for not passing the wine; made several engagements to go to Oxford; announced that I meant to have a dinner-party exactly like that, once a week until further notice; and madly took so much snuff out of Grainger's box, that I was obliged to go into the pantry, and have a private fit of sneezing ten minutes long.

I went on, by passing the wine faster and faster yet, and continually starting up with a corkscrew to open more wine, long before any was needed. I proposed Steerforth's health. I said he was my dearest friend, the protector of my boyhood, and the companion of my prime. I said I was delighted to propose his health. I said I owed him more obligations that I could ever repay, and held him in a higher admiration than I could ever express. I finished by saying, "I'll give you Steerforth! God bless him! Hurrah!" We gave him three times three, and another, and a good one to finish with. I broke my glass in going round the table to shake hands with him, and I said (in two words) "Steerforth, you'retheguidingstarofmyexistence."

I went on, by finding suddenly that somebody was in the middle of a song. Markham was the singer, and he sang "When the heart of a man is depressed with care." He said, when he had sung it, he would give us "Woman!" I took objection to that, and I couldn't allow it. I said it was not a respectful way of proposing the toast, and I would never permit that toast to be drunk in my house otherwise than as "The Ladies!" I was very high with him, mainly I think because I saw Steerforth and Grainger laughing at me–or at him–or at both of us. He said a man was not to be dictated to. I said a man *was*. He said a man was not to be insulted, then. I said he was right there–never under my roof, where the Lares were sacred, and the laws of hospitality paramount. He said it was no derogation from a man's dignity to confess that I was a devilish good fellow. I instantly proposed his health.

Somebody was smoking. We were all smoking. *I* was smoking, and trying to suppress a rising tendency to shudder. Steerforth had made a speech about me, in the course of which I had been affected almost to tears. I returned thanks, and hoped the present company would dine with me to-morrow, and the day after–each day at five o'clock, that we might enjoy the pleasures of conversation and society through a long evening. I felt called upon to propose an individual. I would give them my aunt. Miss Betsey Trotwood, the best of her sex!

Somebody was leaning out of my bed-room window, refreshing his forehead against the cool stone of the parapet, and feeling the air upon his face. It was myself. I was addressing myself as "Copperfield," and saying, "Why did you try to smoke? You might have known you couldn't do it." Now, somebody was unsteadily contemplating his features in the looking glass. That was I too. I was very pale in the looking-glass; my eyes had a vacant appearance; and my hair–only my hair, nothing else–looked drunk.

Somebody said to me, "Let us go to the theatre, Copperfield!" There was no bed-room before me, but again the jingling table covered with glasses; the lamp; Grainger on my right hand, Markham on my left, and Steerforth opposite–all sitting in a mist, and a long way off. The theatre? To be sure. The very thing. Come along! But they must excuse me if I saw everybody out first, and turned the lamp off–in case of fire.

Owing to some confusion in the dark, the door was gone. I was feeling for it in the window-curtains, when Steerforth, laughing, took me by the arm and led me out. We went down-stairs, one behind another. Near the bottom, somebody fell, and rolled down. Somebody else said it was Copperfield. I was angry at that false report, until, finding myself on my back in the passage, I began to think there might be some foundation for it.

A very foggy night, with great rings round the lamps in the streets! There was an indistinct talk of its being wet. *I* considered it frosty. Steerforth

dusted me under a lamp-post, and put my hat into shape, which somebody produced from somewhere in a most extraordinary manner, for I hadn't had it on before. Steerforth then said, "You are all right, Copperfield, are you not?" and I told him, "Neverberrer."

Nephew Fred's Flat

A Christmas Carol, Stave Thre

This is but a brief passage from the long scene which altogether is an inspiring picture of the popular games and other amusements which are enjoyed in Fred's flat on Christmas Day.

After tea, they had some music. For they were a musical family, and knew what they were about, when they sung a Glee or Catch, I can assure you: especially Topper, who could growl away in the bass like a good one, and never swell the large veins in his forehead, or get red in the face over it. Scrooge's niece played well upon the harp ; and played among other tunes a simple little air (a mere nothing : you might learn to whistle it in two minutes), which had been familiar to the child who fetched Scrooge from the boarding-school, as he had been reminded by the Ghost of Christmas Past. When this strain of music sounded, all the things that Ghost had shown him, came upon his mind; he softened more and more; and thought that if he could have listened to it often, years ago, he might have cultivated the kindnesses of life for his own happiness with his own hands, without resorting to the sexton's spade that buried Jacob Marley.

But they didn't devote the whole evening to music. After a while they played at forfeits ; for it is good to be children sometimes, and never better than at Christmas, when its mighty Founder was child himself. Stop! There was first a game at blind-man's buff. Of course there was. And I no more believe Topper was really blind than I believe he had eyes in his boots. My opinion is, that it was a done thing between him and Scrooge's nephew; and that the Ghost of Christmas Present knew it. The way he went after that plump sister in the lace tucker, was an outrage on the credulity of human nature. Knocking down the fire-irons, tumbling over the chairs, bumping up against the piano, smothering himself among the curtains, wherever she went, there went he. He always knew where the plump sister was. He wouldn't catch anybody else. If you had fallen up against him (as some of them did) on purpose, he would have made a feint of endeavouring to seize you, which would have been an affront to your understanding, and would instantly have sidled off in the direction of the plump sister. She often cried out that it wasn't fair; and it really was not. But when at last, he caught her; when, in spite of all her silken rustlings, and her rapid flutterings past him, he got her into a corner whence there was no escape; then his conduct was the most execrable. For his pretending not to know her; his pretending that it was necessary to touch her head-dress, and further to assure himself of her identity by pressing a certain ring upon her finger, and a certain chain about her neck; was vile, monstrous! No doubt she told him her opinion of it, when, another blind-man being in office, they were so very confidential together, behind the curtains.

Nettie Quinn Puppets and Marrionettes

Old Curiosity Shop, Chapter 16

As Nell and her grandfather are traveling through the countryside, they discover these puppetteers in a graveyard making repairs.

They were two men who were seated in easy attitudes upon the grass, and so busily engaged as to be at first unconscious of intruders. It was not difficult to divine that they were of a class of itinerant showmen–exhibitors of the freaks of Punch–for, perched cross-legged upon a tombstone behind them, was a figure of that hero himself, his nose and chin as hooked and his face as beaming as usual. Perhaps his imperturbable character was never more strikingly developed, for he preserved his usual equable smile notwithstanding that his body was dangling in a most uncomfortable position, all loose and limp and shapeless, while his long peaked cap, unequally balanced against his exceedingly slight legs, threatened every instant to bring him toppling down.

In part scattered upon the ground at the feet of the two men, and in part jumbled together in a long flat box, were the other persons of the Drama. The hero's wife and one child, the hobby-horse, the doctor, the foreign gentleman who not being familiar with the language is unable in the representation to express his ideas otherwise than by the utterance of the word 'Shallabalah' three distinct times, the radical neighbour who will by no means admit that a tin bell is an organ, the executioner, and the devil, were all here. Their owners had evidently come to that spot to make some needful repairs in the stage arrangements, for one of them was engaged in binding together a small gallows with thread, while the other was intent upon fixing a new black wig, with the aid of a small hammer and some tacks, upon the head of the radical neighbour, who had been beaten bald.

They raised their eyes when the old man and his young companion were close upon them, and pausing in their work, returned their looks of curiosity. One of them, the actual exhibitor no doubt, was a little merry-faced man with a twinkling eye and a red nose, who seemed to have unconsciously imbibed something of his hero's character. The other–that was he who took the money–had rather a careful and cautious look, which was perhaps inseparable from his occupation also.

The merry man was the first to greet the strangers with a nod; and following the old man's eyes, he observed that perhaps that was the first time he had ever seen a Punch off the stage. (Punch, it may be remarked, seemed to be pointing with the tip of his cap to a most flourishing epitaph, and to be chuckling over it with all his heart.)

"Why do you come here to do this?" said the old man, sitting down beside them, and looking at the figures with extreme delight.

"Why you see," rejoined the little man, "we're putting up for to-night at the public-house yonder, and it wouldn't do to let 'em see the present company undergoing repair."

"No!" cried the old man, making signs to Nell to listen, "why not, eh? why not?"

"Because it would destroy all the delusion, and take away all the interest, wouldn't it?" replied the little man. "Would you care a ha'penny for the Lord Chancellor if you know'd him in private and without his wig?–certainly not."

"Good!" said the old man, venturing to touch one of the puppets, and drawing away his hand with a shrill laugh. "Are you going to show 'em to-night? are you?"

"That is the intention, governor," replied the other, "and unless I'm much mistaken, Tommy Codlin is a calculating at this minute what we've lost through your coming upon us. Cheer up, Tommy, it can't be much."

The little man accompanied these latter words with a wink, expressive of the estimate he had formed of the travellers' finances.

To this Mr. Codlin, who had a surly, grumbling manner, replied, as he twitched Punch off the tombstone and flung him into the box,

"I don't care if we haven't lost a farden, but you're too free. If you stood in front of the curtain and see the public's faces as I do, you'd know human natur' better."

"Ah! it's been the spoiling of you, Tommy, your taking to that branch," rejoined his companion. "When you played the ghost in the reg'lar drama in the fairs, you believed in everything–except ghosts. But now you're a universal mistruster. *I* never see a man so changed."

"Never mind," said Mr. Codlin, with the air of a discontented philosopher. "I know better now, and p'raps I'm sorry for it."

Turning over the figures in the box like one who knew and despised them, Mr. Codlin drew one forth and held it up for the inspection of his friend:

"Look here; here's all this Judy's clothes falling to pieces again. You haven't got a needle and thread I suppose?"

The little man shook his head, and scratched it ruefully as he contemplated this severe indisposition of a principal performer. Seeing that they were at a loss, the child said timidly:

"I have a needle, sir, in my basket, and thread too. Will you let me try to mend it for you? I think I could do it neater than you could."

Even Mr. Codlin had nothing to urge against a proposal so seasonable. Nelly, kneeling down beside the box, was soon busily engaged in her task, and accomplishing it to a miracle.

While she was thus engaged, the merry little man looked at her with an interest which did not appear to be diminished when he glanced at her helpless companion. When she had finished her work he thanked her, and inquired whither they were travelling.

"N–no further to-night, I think," said the child, looking towards her grandfather.

"If you're wanting a place to stop at," the man remarked, "I should advise you to take up at the same house with us. That's it. The long, low, white house there. It's very cheap."

Nicholas Nickleby and Kate

Nicholas Nickleby, Chapter 3, Chapter 54

In the first passage, Nicholas is contrasted with his uncle Ralph; in the second, with his sister Kate.

Mrs. Nickleby made no other reply than entreating Nicholas by a gesture to keep silent; and the uncle and nephew looked at each other for some seconds without speaking. The face of the old man was stern, hard-featured, and forbidding; that of the young one, open, handsome, and ingenuous. The old man's eye was keen with the twinklings of avarice and cunning; the young man's, bright with the light of intelligence and spirit. His figure was somewhat slight, but manly and well-formed; and, apart from all the grace of youth and comeliness, there was an emanation from the warm young heart in his look and bearing which kept the old man down.

However striking such a contrast as this may be to lookers-on, none ever feel it with half the keenness or acuteness of perception with which it strikes to the very soul of him whose inferiority it marks. It galled Ralph to the heart's core, and he hated Nicholas from that hour.

* * *

As the brother and sister stood side by side, with a gallant bearing which became them well, a close likeness between them was apparent, which many, had they only seen them apart, might have failed to remark. The air, carriage, and very look and expression of the brother were all reflected in the sister, but softened and refined to the nicest limit of feminine delicacy and attraction. More striking still, was some indefinable resemblance in the face of Ralph, to both. While they had never looked more handsome, nor he more ugly; while they had never held themselves more proudly, nor he shrunk half so low; there never had been a time when this resemblance was so perceptible, or when all the worst characteristics of a face rendered coarse and harsh by evil thoughts were half so manifest as now.

Nicholas Nickleby Cottage

Nicholas Nickleby, Chapter 35

The Cheeryble Brothers offer to rent to the Nickleby family a small cottage.

And I think, my dear brother," said Nicholas's first friend, "that if we were to let them that little cottage at Bow which is empty, at something under the usual rent, now? Eh, brother Ned?"

"For nothing at all," said brother Ned. "We are rich, and should be ashamed to touch the rent under such circumstances as these. Where is Tim Linkinwater?–for nothing at all, my dear brother, for nothing at all."

"Perhaps it would be better to say something, brother Ned," suggested the other, mildly; "it would help to preserve habits of frugality, you know, and remove any painful sense of overwhelming obligations. We might say fifteen pound, or twenty pound, and if it was punctually paid, make it up to them in some other way. And I might secretly advance a small loan towards a little furniture, and you might secretly advance another small loan, brother Ned; and if we find them doing well–as we shall; there's no fear, no fear–we can change the loan into gifts. Carefully, brother Ned, and by degrees, and without pressing upon them too much; what do you say now, brother?"

Brother Ned gave his hand upon it, and not only said it should he done, but had it done too; and, in one short week, Nicholas took possession of the stool, and Mrs. Nickleby and Kate took possession of the house, and all was hope, bustle, and light-heartedness.

There surely never was such a week of discoveries and surprises as the first week of that cottage. Every night when Nicholas came home, something new had been found out. One day it was a grape vine, and another day it was a boiler, and another day it was the key of the front parlour closet at the bottom of the water-butt, and so on through a hundred items. Then, this room was embellished with a muslin curtain, and that room was rendered quite elegant by a window-blind, and such improvements were made, as no one would have supposed possible. Then there was Miss La Creevy, who had come out in the omnibus to stop a day or two and help, and who was perpetually losing a very small brown paper parcel of tin tacks and a very large hammer, and running about with her sleeves tucked up at the wrists, and falling off pairs of steps and hurting herself very much–and Mrs. Nickleby, who talked incessantly, and did something now and then, but not often–and Kate, who busied herself noiselessly everywhere, and was pleased with everything–and Smike, who made the garden a perfect wonder to look upon–and Nicholas, who helped and encouraged them every one–all the peace and cheerfulness of home restored, with such new zest imparted to every frugal pleasure, and such delight to every hour of meeting, as misfortune and separation alone could give!

Norman Church

A Christmas Carol, Stave Four

Here we see the unforgettable churchyard where Scrooge is redeemed by his memories.

A churchyard. Here, then, the wretched man whose name he had now to learn, lay underneath the ground. It was a worthy place. Walled in by houses; overrun by grass and weeds, the growth of vegetation's death, not life; choked up with too much burying; fat with repleted appetite. A worthy place!

The Spirit stood among the graves, and pointed down to One. He advanced towards it trembling. The Phantom was exactly as it had been, but he dreaded that he saw new meaning in its solemn shape.

"Before I draw nearer to that stone to which you point," said Scrooge, "answer me one question. Are these the shadows of the things that Will be, or are they shadows of the things that May be, only?"

Still the Ghost pointed downward to the grave by which it stood.

"Men's courses will foreshadow certain ends, to which, if persevered in, they must lead," said Scrooge. "But if the courses be departed from, the ends will change. Say it is thus with what you show me!"

The Spirit was immovable as ever.

Scrooge crept towards it, trembling as he went; and following the finger, read upon the stone of the neglected grave his own name, Ebenezer Scrooge.

The Olde Camden Town Church

The Uncommercial Traveller, "City of London Churches"

Dickens lived in Camden as a boy just as the Cratchit family does. This old church in that district is one of several visited in this touching essay.

So many bells are ringing, when I stand undecided at a street corner, that every sheep in the ecclesiastical fold might be a bell-wether. The discordance is fearful. My state of indecision is referable to, and about equally divisible among, four great churches, which are all within sight and sound, all within the space of a few square yards.

As I stand at the street corner, I don't see as many as four people at once going to church, though I see as many as four churches with their steeples clamouring for people. I choose my church, and go up the flight of steps to the great entrance in the tower. A mouldy tower within, and like a neglected washhouse. A rope comes through the beamed roof, and a man in the corner pulls it and clashes the bell–a whity-brown man, whose clothes were once black–a man with flue on him, and cobweb. He stares at me, wondering how I come there, and I stare at him, wondering how he comes there. Through a screen of wood and glass, I peep into the dim church. About twenty people are discernible, waiting to begin. Christening would seem to have faded out of this church long ago, for the font has the dust of desuetude thick upon it, and its wooden cover (shaped like an old fashioned tureen-cover) looks as if it wouldn't come off, upon requirement. I perceive the altar to be rickety and the Commandments damp. Entering after this survey, I jostle the clergyman in his canonicals, who is entering too from a dark lane behind a pew of state with curtains, where nobody sits. The pew is ornamented with four blue wands, once carried by four somebodys, I suppose, before somebody else, but which there is nobody now to hold or receive honour from. I open the door of a family pew, and shut myself in; if I could occupy twenty family pews at once I might have them.

Old Curiosity Shop

Old Curiosity Shop, Chapter I

The Curiosity Shop is the place from where Nell and her grandfather begin their long journey.

He was a little old man with long grey hair, whose face and figure, as he held the light above his head and looked before him as he approached, I could plainly see. Though much altered by age, I fancied I could recognise in his spare and slender form something of that delicate mould which I had noticed in the child. Their bright blue eyes were certainly alike, but his face was so deeply furrowed, and so very full of care, that here all resemblance ceased.

The place through which he made his way at leisure, was one of those receptacles for old and curious things which seem to crouch in odd corners of this town, and to hide their musty treasures from the public eye in jealousy and distrust. There were suits of mail standing like ghosts in armour, here and there; fantastic carvings brought from monkish cloisters; rusty weapons of various kinds; distorted figures in china, and wood, and iron, and ivory; tapestry, and strange furniture that might have been designed in dreams. The haggard aspect of the little old man was wonderfully suited to the place; he might have groped among old churches, and tombs, and deserted houses, and gathered all the spoils with his own hands. There was nothing in the whole collection but was in keeping with himself; nothing that looked older or more worn than he.

As he turned the key in the lock, he surveyed me with some astonishment, which was not diminished when he looked from me to my companion. The door being opened, the child addressed him as her grandfather, and told him the little story of our companionship.

"Why bless thee, child," said the old man patting her on the head, "how couldst thou miss thy way? What if I had lost thee, Nell!"

"I would have found my way back to *you*, grandfather," said the child boldly: "never fear."

The Old Globe Theatre

Great Expectations, Chapter 31

Pip and his friend attend the London debut of a childhood acquaintance, Mr. Wopsle, as Hamlet. The earnest performance and rude critique of the audience are described in such detail, one must wonder if Dickens didn't see the performance himself.

On our arrival in Denmark, we found the king and queen of that country elevated in two arm-chairs on a kitchen-table, holding a Court. The whole of the Danish nobility were in attendance; consisting of a noble boy in the wash-leather boots of a gigantic ancestor, a venerable Peer with a dirty face, who seemed to have risen from the people late in life, and the Danish chivalry with a comb in its hair and a pair of white silk legs, and presenting on the whole a feminine appearance. My gifted townsman stood gloomily apart, with folded arms, and I could have wished that his curls and forehead had been more probable.

Several curious little circumstances transpired as the action proceeded. The late king of the country not only appeared to have been troubled with a cough at the time of his decease, but to have taken it with him to the tomb, and to have brought it back. The royal phantom also carried a ghostly manuscript round its truncheon, to which it had the appearance of occasionally referring, and that, too, with an air of anxiety and a tendency to lose the place of reference which were suggestive of a state of mortality. It was this, I conceive, which led to the Shade's being advised by the gallery to "turn over!"–a recommendation which it took extremely ill. It was likewise to be noted of this majestic spirit that whereas it always appeared with an air of having been out a long time and walked an immense distance, it perceptibly came from a closely-contiguous wall. This occasioned its terrors to be received derisively. The Queen of Denmark, a very buxom lady, though no doubt historically brazen, was considered by the public to have too much brass about her; her chin being attached to her diadem by a broad band of that metal (as if she had a gorgeous toothache), her waist being encircled by another, and each of her arms by another, so that she was openly mentioned as "the kettledrum." The noble boy in the ancestral boots, was inconsistent; representing himself, as it were in one breath, as an able seaman, a strolling actor, a gravedigger, a clergyman, and a person of the utmost importance at a Court fencing-match, on the authority of whose practised eye and nice discrimination the finest strokes were judged. This gradually led to a want of toleration for him, and even–on his being detected in holy orders, and declining to perform the funeral service–to the general indignation taking the form of nuts. Lastly, Ophelia was a prey to such slow musical madness, that when, in course of time, she had taken off her white muslin scarf, folded it up, and buried it, a sulky man who had been long cooling his impatient nose against an iron bar in the front row of the gallery, growled, "Now the baby's put to bed, let's have supper!" Which, to say the least of it, was out of keeping.

Upon my unfortunate townsman all these incidents accumulated with playful effect. Whenever that undecided Prince had to ask a question or state a doubt, the public helped him out with it. As for example; on the question whether 'twas nobler in the mind to suffer, some roared yes, and some no, and some inclining to both opinions said "toss up for it;" and quite a Debating Society arose. When he asked what should such fellows as he do crawling between earth and heaven, he was encouraged with loud cries of "Hear, hear !" When he appeared with his stocking disordered (its disorder expressed, according to usage, by one very neat fold in the top, which I suppose to be always got up with a flat iron), a conversation took place in the gallery respecting the paleness of his leg, and whether it was occasioned by the turn the ghost had given him. On his taking the recorders–very like a little black flute that had just been played in the orchestra and handed out at the door–he was called upon unanimously for Rule Britannia. When he recommended the player not to saw the air thus, the sulky man said, "And don't *you* do it, neither; you're a deal worse than *him*!" And I grieve to add that peals of laughter greeted Mr. Wopsle on every one of these occasions.

But his greatest trials were in the churchyard: which had the appearance of a primeval forest, with a kind of small ecclesiastical wash-house on one side, and a turnpike gate on the other. Mr. Wopsle, in a comprehensive black cloak, being descried entering at the turnpike, the gravedigger was admonished in a friendly way, "Look out! Here's the undertaker a coming, to see how you're getting on with your work!" I believe it is well known in a constitutional country that Mr. Wopsle could not possibly have returned the skull, after moralising over it, without dusting his fingers on a white napkin taken from his breast; but even that innocent and indispensable action did not pass without the comment "Wai-ter!" The arrival of the body for interment (in an empty black box with the lid tumbling open), was the signal for a general joy which was much enhanced by the discovery, among the bearers, of an individual obnoxious to identification. The joy attended Mr. Wopsle through his struggle with Laertes on the brink of the orchestra and the grave, and slackened no more until he had tumbled the king off the kitchen-table, and had died by inches from the ankles upward.

Old Michaelchurch

The Uncommercial Traveller, "The City of the Absent"

Here is a churchyard Dickens must have loved. It is beautiful country place, now surrounded by that oldest district of London, called "The City."

Such strange churchyards hide in the City of London; churchyards sometimes so entirely detached from churches, always so pressed upon by houses; so small, so rank, so silent, so forgotten, except by a few people who ever look down into them from their smoky windows. As I stand peeping in through the iron gates and rails, I can peel the rusty metal off, like bark from an old tree. The illegible tombstones are all lop-sided, the grave-mounds lost their shape in the rains of a hundred years ago, the Lombardy Poplar or Plane-Tree that was once a drysalter's daughter and several common-councilmen, has withered like those worthies, and its departed leaves are dust beneath it. Contagion of slow ruin overhangs the place. The discoloured tiled roofs of the environing buildings stand so awry, that they can hardly be proof against any stress of weather. Old crazy stacks of chimneys seem to look down as they overhang, dubiously calculating how far they will have to fall. In an angle of the walls, what was once the tool-house of the grave-digger rots away, encrusted with toadstools. Pipes and spouts for carrying off the rain from the encompassing gables, broken or feloniously cut for old lead long ago, now let the rain drip and splash as it list, upon the weedy earth. Sometimes there is a rusty pump somewhere near, and as I look in at the rails and meditate, I hear it working under an unknown hand with a creaking protest: as though the departed in the churchyard urged, "Let us lie here in peace; don't suck us up and drink us!"

Peggotty's Seaside Cottage

David Copperfield, Chapter 3

The most unusual building Dickens created is the beached boat which provides a home to Mr. Peggotty and his extended family, each of them the survivor of wrecks of various kinds. The original illustration of this scene is one of the very few times when the opinion of the artist prevailed contrary to Dickens' description.

Ham carrying me on his back and a small box of ours under his arm, and Peggotty carrying another small box of ours, we turned down lanes bestrewn with bits of chips and little hillocks of sand, and went past gas-works, rope-walks, boat-builders' yards, ship-wrights' yards, ship-breakers' yards, caulkers' yards, riggers' lofts, smiths' forges, and a great litter of such places, until we came out upon the dull waste I had already seen at a distance; when Ham said,

"Yon's our house, Mas'r Davy!"

I looked in all directions, as far as I could stare over the wilderness, and away at the sea, and away at the river, but no house could *I* make out. There was a black barge, or some other kind of superannuated boat, not far off, high and dry on the ground, with an iron funnel sticking out of it for a chimney and smoking very cosily; but nothing else in the way of a habitation that was visible to *me*.

"That's not it? said I. "That ship-looking thing?"

"That's it, Mas'r Davy," returned Ham.

If it had been Aladdin's palace, roc's egg and all, I suppose I could not have been more charmed with the romantic idea of living in it. There was a delightful door cut in the side, and it was roofed in, and there were little windows in it; but the wonderful charm of it was, that it was a real boat which had no doubt been upon the water hundreds of times, and which had never been intended to be lived in, on dry land. That was the captivation of it to me. If it had ever been meant to be lived in, I might have thought it small, or inconvenient, or lonely; but never having been designed for any such use, it became a perfect abode.

It was beautifully clean inside, and as tidy as possible. There was a table, and a Dutch clock, and a chest of drawers, and on the chest of drawers there was a tea-tray with a painting on it of a lady with a parasol, taking a walk with a military-looking child who was trundling a hoop. The tray was kept from tumbling down, by a bible; and the tray, if it had tumbled down, would have smashed a quantity of cups and saucers and a teapot that were grouped around the book. On the walls there were some common coloured pictures, framed and glazed, of scripture subjects; such as I have never seen since in the hands of pedlars, without seeing the whole interior of Peggotty's brother's house again, at one view. Abraham in red going to sacrifice Isaac in blue, and Daniel in yellow cast into a den of green lions, were the most prominent of these. Over the little mantel-shelf, was a picture of the Sarah Jane lugger, built at Sunderland, with a real little wooden stern stuck on to it; a work of art, combining composition with carpentry, which I considered to be one of the most enviable possessions that the world could afford. There were some hooks in the beams of the ceiling, the use of which I did not divine then; and some lockers and boxes and conveniences of that sort, which served for seats and eked out the chairs.

All this, I saw in the first glance after I crossed the threshhold–child-like, according to my theory–then Peggotty opened a little door and showed me my bedroom. It was the completest and most desirable bedroom ever seen–in the stern of the vessel; with a little window, where the rudder used to go through; a little looking-glass, just the right height for me, nailed against the wall, and framed with oyster-shells; a little bed, which there was just room enough to get into; and a nosegay of seaweed in a blue mug on the table. The walls were whitewashed as white as milk, and the patchwork counterpane made my eyes quite ache with its brightness.

Pied Bull Inn

The Uncommercial Traveller, "An Old Stage Coaching House"

The coaching inns had their days of glory, and the railroad ended them. Here Dickens painfully describes such an inn in its decay, yet shows us as well how the inn was in life. How similar this description is to those of decaying grand temples of railroad stations, similarly disused after the coming of freeways.

At the Railway Station seven miles off, I had been the subject of wonder when I ordered a fly in which to come here. And when I gave the direction " To the Dolphin's Head," I had observed an ominous stare on the countenance of the strong young man in velveteen, who was the platform servant of the Company. He had also called to my driver at parting, "All ri-ight ! Don't hang yourself when you get there, Geo-o-rge!" in a sarcastic tone, for which I had entertained some transitory thoughts of reporting him to the General Manager.

I had no business in the town–I never have any business in any town–but I had been caught by the fancy that I would come and look at it in its degeneracy. My purpose was fitly inaugurated by the Dolphin's Head, which everywhere expressed past coachfulness and present coachlessness. Coloured prints of coaches, starting, arriving, changing horses, coaches in the sunshine, coaches in the snow, coaches in the wind, coaches in the mist and rain, coaches on the King's birthday, coaches in all circumstances compatible with their triumph and victory, but never in the act of breaking down or overturning, pervaded the house. Of these works of art, some, frame and not glazed, had holes in them ; the varnish of others had become so brown and cracked, that they looked like overdone pie-crust ; the designs of others were almost obliterated by the flies of many summers. Broken glasses, damaged frames, lop-sided hanging, and consignment of incurable cripples to places of refuge in dark corners, attested the desolation of the rest. The old room on the ground floor where the passengers of the Highflyer used to dine, had nothing in it but a wretched show of twigs and flower-pots in the broad window to hide the nakedness of the land, and in a corner little Mellows's perambulator, with even its parasol-head turned despondently to the wall. The other room, where post-horse company used to wait while relays were getting ready down the yard, still held its ground, but was as airless as I conceive a hearse to be: insomuch that Mr. Pitt, hanging high against the partition (with spots on him like port wine, though it is mysterious how port wine ever got squirted up there), had good reason for perking his nose and sniffing. The stopperless cruets on the spindle-shanked sideboard were in a miserably dejected state: the anchovy sauce having turned blue some years ago, and the cayenne pepper (with a scoop in it like a small model of a wooden leg) having turned solid. The old fraudulent candles which were always being paid for and never used, were burnt out at last ; but their tall stilts of candlesticks still lingered, and still outraged the human intellect by pretending to be silver. The mouldy old unreformed Borough Member, with his right hand buttoned up in the breast of his coat, and his back characteristically turned on bales of petitions from his constituents, was there too; and the poker which never had been among the fire-irons, lest post-horse company should overstir the fire, was *not* there, as of old.

Pursuing my researches in the Dolphin's Head, I found it sorely shrunken. When J. Mellows came into possession, he had walled off half the bar, which was now a tobacco-shop with its own entrance in the yard–the once glorious yard where the post-boys, whip in hand and always buttoning their waistcoats at the last moment, used to come running forth to mount and away. A "Scientific Shoeing-Smith and Veterinary Surgeon," had further encroached upon the yard ; and a grimly satirical Jobber, who announced himself as having to Let "A neat one-horse fly, and a one-horse cart," had established his business, himself, and his family, in a part of the extensive stables. Another part was lopped clean off from the Dolphin's Head, and now comprised a chapel, a wheelwright's, and a Young Men's Mutual Improvement and Discussion Society (in a loft): the whole forming a back lane. No audacious hand had plucked down the vane from the central cupola of the stables, but it had grown rusty and stuck at N–Nil : while the score or two of pigeons that remained true to their ancestral traditions and the place, had collected in a row on the roof-ridge of the only outhouse retained by the Dolphin, where all the inside pigeons tried to push the outside pigeon off. This I accepted as emblematical of the struggle for post and place in railway times.

Sauntering forth into the town, by way of the covered and pillared entrance to the Dolphin's Yard, once redolent of soup and stable-litter, now redolent of musty disuse, I paced the street. It was a hot day, and the little sun-blinds of the shops were all drawn down, and the more enterprising tradesmen had caused their 'Prentices to trickle water on the pavement appertaining to their frontage. It looked as if they had been shedding tears for the stage-coaches, and drying their ineffectual pocket-handkerchiefs. Such weakness would have been excusable ; for business was–as one dejected porkman who kept a shop which refused to reciprocate the compliment by keeping him, informed me–"bitter bad." Most of the harness-makers and corn-dealers were gone the way of the coaches, but it was a pleasant recognition of the eternal procession of Children down that old original steep Incline, the Valley of the Shadow, that those tradesmen were mostly succeeded by vendors of sweetmeats and cheap toys. The opposition house to the Dolphin, once famous as the New White Hart, had long collapsed. In a fit of abject depression, it had cast whitewash on its windows, and boarded up its front door, and reduced itself to a side entrance; but even that had proved a world too wide for the Literary Institution which had been its last phase; for the Institution had collapsed too, and of the ambitious letters of its inscription on the White Hart's front, all had fallen off but these:

L Y INS T

–suggestive of Lamentably Insolvent. As to the neighbouring market-place, it seemed to have wholly relinquished marketing, to the dealer in crockery whose pots and pans straggled half across it, and to the Cheap Jack who sat with folded arms on the shafts of his cart, superciliously gazing around; his velveteen waistcoat, evidently harbouring grave doubts whether it was worth his while to stay a night in such a place.

The church bells began to ring as I left this spot, but they by no means improved the case, for they said, in a petulant way, and speaking with some difficulty in their irritation, "WHAT'S-be-come-of-THE-coach-ES!" Nor would they (I found on listening) ever vary their emphasis, save in respect of growing more sharp and vexed, but invariably went on, "WHAT'S-be-come-of-THE-coach-ES!"–always beginning the inquiry with an unpolite abruptness. Perhaps from their elevation they saw the railway, and it aggravated them.

The Poulterer

A Christmas Carol, Stave Five

The Poulterer, of course, is where Scrooge buys the prize turkey that he gives to Bob Cratchit.

Running to the window, he opened it, and put out his head. No fog, no mist; clear, bright, jovial, stirring, cold; cold, piping for the blood to dance to; Golden sunlight; Heavenly sky; sweet fresh air; merry bells. Oh, glorious. Glorious!

"What's to day!" cried Scrooge, calling downward to a boy in Sunday clothes, who perhaps had loitered in to look about him.

"EH?" returned the boy, with all his might of wonder.

"What's to-day, my fine fellow?" said Scrooge.

"To-day!" replied the boy. "Why, Christmas Day."

"It's Christmas Day!" said Scrooge to himself. I haven't missed it. The Spirits have done it all in one night. They can do anything they like. Of course they can. Of course they can. Hallo, my fine fellow!"

" Hallo!" returned the boy.

"Do you know the Poulterer's, in the next street but one, at the corner?" Scrooge inquired.

"I should hope I did," replied the lad.

"An intelligent boy!" said Scrooge. "A remarkable boy! Do you know whether they've sold the prize Turkey that was hanging up there?–Not the little prize Turkey: the big one?"

"What, the one as big as me?" returned the boy.

"What a delightful boy!" said Scrooge. "It's a pleasure to talk to him. Yes, my buck!"

"It's hanging there now," replied the boy.

"Is it? " said Scrooge. "Go and buy it."

"Walk-ER!" exclaimed the boy.

"No, no," said Scrooge, "I am in earnest. Go and buy it, and tell 'em to bring it here, that I may give them the direction where to take it. Come back with the man, and I'll give you a shilling. Come back with him in less than five minutes and I'll give you half-a-crown!"

The boy was off like a shot. He must have had a steady hand at a trigger who could have got a shot off half so fast.

"I'll send it to Bob Cratchit's! " whispered Scrooge, rubbing his hands, and splitting with a laugh. "He sha'n't know who sends it. It's twice the size of Tiny Tim. Joe Miller never made such a joke as sending it to Bob's will be!"

The hand in which he wrote the address was not a steady one, but write it he did, somehow, and went down-stairs to open the street door, ready for the coming of the poulterer's man. As he stood there, waiting his arrival, the knocker caught his eye.

"I shall love it, as long as I live!" cried Scrooge, patting it with his hand. "I scarcely ever looked at it before. What an honest expression it has in its face! It's a wonderful knocker!–Here's the Turkey. Hallo! Whoop! How are you! Merry Christmas!"

It *was* a Turkey! He never could have stood upon his legs, that bird. He would have snapped 'em short off in a minute, like sticks of sealing-wax.

Ramsford Palace

Old Curiosity Shop, Chapter 40

The nobility are objects of sarcasm for Dickens. Here we have a scene with someone who thinks the lives of the rich and famous are worthy of discussion at dinner parties.

At this repast, Mr. Chuckster exerted his utmost abilities to en-chant his entertainers, and impress them with a conviction of the mental superiority of those who dwelt in town; with which view he led the discourse to the small scandal of the day, in which he was justly considered by his friends to shine prodigiously. Thus, he was in a condition to relate the exact circumstances of the difference between the Marquis of Mizzler and Lord Bobby, which it appeared originated in a disputed bottle of champagne, and not in a pigeon-pie, as erroneously reported in the newspapers; neither had Lord Bobby said to the Marquis of Mizzler, "Mizzler, one of us two tells a lie, and I'm not the man," as incorrectly stated by the same authorities; but "Mizzler, you know where I'm to be found, and damme, sir, find me if you want me"–which, of course, entirely changed the aspect of this interesting question, and placed it in a very different light. He also acquainted them with the precise amount of the income guaranteed by the Duke of Thigsberry to Violetta Stetta of the Italian Opera, which it appeared was payable quarterly, and not half-yearly, as the public had been given to understand, and which was *ex*clusive, and not *in*clusive, (as had been monstrously stated,) of jewellery, perfumery, hair-powder for five footmen, and two daily changes of kid-gloves for a page. Having entreated the old lady and gentleman to set their minds at rest on these absorbing points, for they might rely on his statement being the correct one, Mr. Chuckster entertained them with theatrical chit-chat and the court circular; and so wound up a brilliant and fascinating conversation which he had maintained alone, and without any assistance whatever, for upwards of three-quarters of an hour.

Scroogе and Marley

A Christmas Carol, Stave One

Scrooge, one of the most identifiable fictional characters in literature, is introduced to the world.

Marley was dead, to begin with. There is no doubt whatever about that. The register of his burial was signed by the clergy-man, the clerk, the undertaker, and the chief mourner. Scrooge signed it. And Scrooge's name was good upon 'Change, for anything he chose to put his hand to.

Old Marley was as dead as a door-nail.

Mind! I don't mean to say that I know, of my own knowledge, what there is particularly dead about a door-nail. I might have been inclined, myself, to regard a coffin-nail as the deadest piece of ironmongery in the trade. But the wisdom of our ancestors is in the simile; and my unhallowed hands shall not disturb it, or the Country's done for. You will therefore permit me to repeat, emphatically, that Marley was as dead as a door-nail.

Scrooge knew he was dead? Of course he did. How could it be otherwise? Scrooge and he were partners for I don't know how many years. Scrooge was his sole executor, his sole administrator, his sole assign, his sole residuary legatee, his sole friend, and sole mourner. And even Scrooge was not so dreadfully cut up by the sad event, but that he was an excellent man of business on the very day of the funeral, and solemnised it with an undoubted bargain.

The mention of Marley's funeral brings me back to the point I started from. There is no doubt that Marley was dead. This must be distinctly understood, or nothing wonderful can come of the story I am going to relate. If we were not perfectly convinced that Hamlet's Father died before the play began, there would be nothing more remarkable in his taking a stroll at night, in an easterly wind, upon his own ramparts, than there would be in any other middle-aged gentleman rashly turning out after dark in a breezy spot–say Saint Paul's Churchyard for instance–literally to astonish his son's weak mind.

Scrooge never painted out Old Marley's name. There it stood, years afterwards, above the warehouse door: Scrooge and Marley. The firm was known as Scrooge and Marley. Sometimes people new to the business called Scrooge Scrooge, and sometimes Marley, but he answered to both names. It was all the same to him.

Oh! But he was a tight-fisted hand at the grindstone, Scrooge! a squeezing, wrenching, grasping, scraping, clutching, covetous, old sinner! Hard and sharp as flint, from which no steel had ever struck out generous fire; secret, and self-contained, and solitary as an oyster. The cold within him froze his old features, nipped his pointed nose, shrivelled his cheek, stiffened his gait; made his eyes red, his thin lips blue; and spoke out shrewdly in his grating voice. A frosty rime was on his head, and on his eyebrows, and his wiry chin. He carried his own low temperature always about with him; he iced his office in the dog-days; and didn't thaw it one degree at Christmas.

External heat and cold had little influence on Scrooge. No warmth could warm, nor wintry weather chill him. No wind that blew was betterer than he, no falling snow was more intent upon its purpose, no pelting rain less open to entreaty. Foul weather didn't know where to have him. The heaviest rain, and snow, and hail, and sleet, could boast of the advantage over him in only one respect. They often "came down" handsomely, and Scrooge never did.

Stone Bridge

Pickwick Papers, Chapter 5

This lyrical scene and its final aphorism is even more astounding when one realizes Dickens was only twenty-three years old when he wrote it.

Bright and pleasant was the sky, balmy the air, and beautiful the appearance of every object around, as Mr. Pickwick lent over the balustrades of Rochester Bridge, contemplating nature, and waiting for breakfast. The scene was indeed one which might well have charmed a far less reflective mind, than that to which it was presented.

On the left of the spectator lay the ruined wall, broken in many places, and in some, overhanging the narrow beach below in rude and heavy masses. Huge knots of sea-weed hung upon the jagged and pointed stones, trembling in every breath of wind; and the green ivy clung mournfully round the dark and ruined battlements. Behind it rose the ancient castle, its towers roofless, and its massive walls crumbling away, but telling us proudly of its own might and strength, as when, seven hundred years ago, it rang with the clash of arms, or resounded with the noise of feasting and revelry. On either side, the banks of the Medway, covered with corn-fields and pastures, with here and there a windmill, or a distant church, stretched away as far as the eve could see, presenting a rich and varied landscape, rendered more beautiful by the changing shadows which passed swiftly across it, as the thin and half-formed clouds skimmed away in the light of the morning sun. The river, reflecting the clear blue of the sky, glistened and sparkled as it flowed noiselessly on; and the oars of the fishermen dipped into the water with a clear and liquid sound, as the heavy but picturesque boats glided slowly down the stream.

Mr. Pickwick was roused from the agreeable reverie into which he had been led by the objects before him, by a deep sigh, and a touch on his shoulder. He turned round: and the dismal man was at his side.

"Contemplating the scene?" inquired the dismal man.

"I was," said Mr. Pickwick.

"And congratulating yourself on being up so soon?" Mr. Pickwick nodded assent.

"Ah! people need to rise early, to see the sun in all his splendour, for his brightness seldom lasts the day through. The morning of day and the morning of life are but too much alike."

Stone Cottage, Thatched Cottage

Old Curiosity Shop, Chapter 15

N*ell and her grandfather pass many cottages as they enter and leave a country village.*

He awoke refreshed, and they continued their journey. The road was pleasant, lying between beautiful pastures and fields of corn, about which, poised high in the clear blue sky, the lark trilled out her happy song. The air came laden with the fragrance it caught upon its way, and the bees, upborne upon its scented breath, hummed forth their drowsy satisfaction as they floated by.

They were now in the open country; the houses were very few and scattered at long intervals, often miles apart. Occasionally they came upon a cluster of poor cottages, some with a chair or low board put across the open door to keep the scrambling children from the road, others shut up close while all the family were working in the fields. These were often the commencement of a little village: and after an interval came a wheelwright's shed or perhaps a blacksmith's forge; then a thriving farm with sleepy cows lying about the yard, and horses peering over the low wall and scampering away when harnessed horses passed upon the road, as though in triumph at their freedom. There were dull pigs too, turning up the ground in search of dainty food, and grunting their monotonous grumblings as they prowled about, or crossed each other in their quest; plump pigeons skimming round the roof or strutting on the eaves; and ducks and geese, far more graceful in their own conceit, waddling awkwardly about the edges of the pond or sailing glibly on its surface. The farm-yard passed, then came the little inn; the humbler beer-shop; and the village tradesman's; then the lawyer's and the parson's, at whose dread names the beer-shop trembled; the church then peeped out modestly from a clump of

trees; then there were a few more cottages; then the cage, and pound, and not unfrequently, on a bank by the way-side, a deep old dusty well. Then came the trim-hedged fields on either hand, and the open road again. They walked all day, and slept that night at a small cottage where beds were let to travellers. Next morning they were afoot again, and though jaded at first, and very tired, recovered before long and proceeded briskly forward.

A Rest by the Way

"A Rest by the Way." Nell and her grandfather in *The Old Curiosity Shop*.

Theatre Royal

David Copperfield, Chapter 19

F*or hilarious scenes of Victorian theatre, turn to* Nicholas Nickleby *where whole chapters tell the adventures of a theatre company. This passage instead illustrates how Dickens loved theatre. It is said that were it not for a cold that forced him to miss an audition early in life, he may have been an actor instead of a writer.*

Being then, in a pleasant frame of mind,[...] I resolved to go to the play. It was Covent Garden Theatre that I chose; and there, from the back of a centre box, I saw Julius Caesar and the new Pantomime. To have all those noble Romans alive before me, and walking in and out for my entertainment, instead of being the stern taskmasters they had been at school, was a most novel and delightful effect. But the mingled reality and mystery of the whole show, the influence upon me of the poetry, the lights, the music, the company, the smooth stupendous changes of glittering and brilliant scenery, were so dazzling, and opened up such illimitable regions of delight, that when I came out into the rainy street, at twelve o'clock at night, I felt as if I had come from the clouds, where I had been leading a romantic life for ages, to a bawling, splashing, link-lighted, umbrella-struggling, hackney-coach-jostling, patten-clinking, muddy, miserable world.

I had emerged by another door, and stood in the street for a little while, as if I really were a stranger upon earth: but the unceremonious pushing and hustling that I received, soon recalled me to myself, and put me in the road back to the hotel; whither I went, revolving the glorious vision all the way; and where, after some porter and oysters, I sat revolving it still, at past one o'clock, with my eyes on the coffee-room fire.

The Tower of London

A Child's History of England, Chapter 26

This story from Dickens' history is one of many where the Tower is used to imprison the nobility. It takes place in the time of Henry the Seventh.

There was a priest at Oxford of the name of Simons, who had for a pupil a handsome boy named Lambert Simnel, the son of a baker. Partly to gratify his own ambitious ends, and partly to carry out the designs of a secret party formed against the king, this priest declared that his pupil, the boy, was no other than the young Earl of Warwick, who (as everybody might have known) was safely locked up in the Tower of London. The priest and the boy went over to Ireland ; and at Dublin enlisted in their cause all ranks of the people, who seemed to have been generous enough, but exceedingly irrational. The Earl of Kildare, the Governor of Ireland, declared that he believed the boy to be what the priest represented; and the boy, who had been well tutored by the priest, told them such things of his childhood, and gave them so many descriptions of the royal family, that they were perpetually shouting and hurrahing, and drinking his health, and making all kinds of noisy and thirsty demonstrations to express their belief in him. Nor was this feeling confined to Ireland alone; for the Earl of Lincoln, whom the late usurper had named as his successor, went over to the young pretender; and, after holding a secret correspondence with the Dowager Duchess of Burgundy, the sister of Edward the Fourth, who detested the present king and all his race, sailed to Dublin with two thousand German soldiers of her providing. In this promising state of the boy's fortunes, he was crowned there, with a crown taken off the head of a statue of the Virgin Mary; and was then, according to the Irish custom of those days, carried home on the shoulders of a big chieftain possessing a great deal more strength than sense. Father Simons you may be sure, was mighty busy at the coronation.

Ten days afterwards, the Germans and the Irish, and the priest and the boy, and the Earl of Lincoln, all landed in Lancashire to invade England. The king, who had good intelligence of their movements, set up his standard at Nottingham, where vast numbers resorted to him every day, while the Earl of Lincoln could gain but very few. With his small force be tried to make for the town of Newark; but the king's army getting between him and that place, he had no choice but to risk a battle at Stoke. It soon ended in the complete destruction of the pretender's forces, one half of whom were killed; among them, the earl himself. The priest and the baker's boy were taken prisoners. The priest, after confessing the trick, was shut up in prison, where he afterwards died,–suddenly perhaps. The boy was taken into the king's kitchen, and made a turnspit. He was afterwards raised to the station of one of the king's falconers; and so ended this strange imposition.

There seems reason to suspect that the dowager queen–always a restless and busy woman–had had some share in tutoring the baker's son. The king was very angry with her, whether or no. He seized upon her property, and shut her up in a convent at Bermondsey.

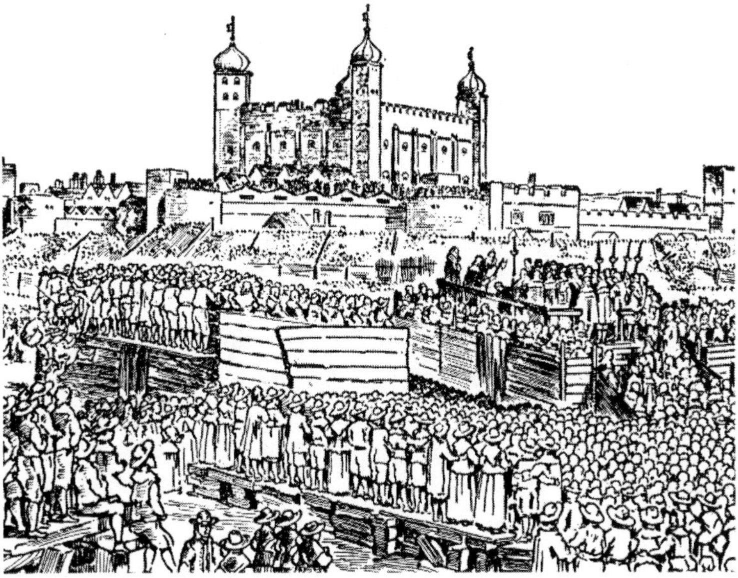

The Execution of the Earl of Stratford. The Tower is in the background. Illustration from a world history textbook published in 1879.

Tuttle's Pub

The Uncommercial Traveller, "Refreshments for Travellers"

Dickens loved inns and coaching stations. He must have visited thousands, and they are frequently the scene of the action in his books. Some inns, however, must have left him less than satisfied, like this one which substitutes atmosphere for quality.

Or, take any other of the numerous travelling instances in which, with more time at your disposal, you are, have been, or may be, equally ill served. Take the old-established Bull's Head with its old-established knife-boxes on its old-established sideboards, its old-established flue under its old-established four-post bedsteads in its old-established airless rooms, its old-established frouziness up-stairs and downstairs, its old-established cookery, and its old-established principles of plunder. Count up your injuries, in its side-dishes of ailing sweet-breads in white poultices, of apothecaries' powders in rice for curry, of pale stewed bits of calf ineffectually relying for an adventitious interest on forcemeat balls. You have had experience of the old-established Bull's Head stringy fowls, with lower extremities like wooden legs, sticking up out of the dish; of its cannibalic boiled mutton, gushing horribly among its capers, when carved; of its little dishes of pastry–roofs of spermaceti ointment, erected over half an apple or four gooseberries. Well for you if you have yet forgotten the old-established Bull's Head fruity port: whose reputation was gained solely by the old-established price the Bull's Head put upon it, and by the old-established air with which the Bull's Head set the glasses and D'Oyleys on, and held that Liquid Gout to the three-and-sixpenny wax-candle, as if its old-established colour hadn't come from the dyer's.

Village Church

Great Expectations, Chapter I

In this scene both comical and touching, Pip describes the graves of his parents and brothers who lie in the yard of his village church.

My father's family name being Pirrip, and my christian name Philip, my infant tongue could make of both names nothing longer or more explicit than Pip. So, I called myself Pip, and came to be called Pip.

I give Pirrip as my father's family name, on the authority of his tombstone and my sister–Mrs. Joe Gargery, who married the blacksmith. As I never saw my father or my mother, and never saw any likeness of either of them (for their days were long before the days of photographs), my first fancies regarding what they were like, were unreasonably derived from their tombstones. The shape of the letters on my father's, gave me an odd idea that he was a square, stout, dark man, with curly black hair. From the character and turn of the inscription, "*Also Georgiana Wife of the Above*," I drew a childish conclusion that my mother was freckled and sickly. To five little stone lozenges, each about a foot and a half long, which were arranged in a neat row beside their grave, and were sacred to the memory of five little brothers of mine–who gave up trying to get a living exceedingly early in that universal struggle–I am indebted for a belief I religiously entertained that they had all been born on their backs with their hands in their trousers-pockets, and had never taken them out in this state of existence.

Ours was the marsh country, down by the river, within, as the river wound, twenty miles of the sea. My first most vivid and broad impression of the identity of things, seems to me to have been gained on a memorable raw afternoon towards evening. At such a time I found out for certain, that this bleak place overgrown with nettles was the churchyard; and that Philip Pirrip, late of this parish, and also Georgiana wife of the above, were dead and buried; and that Alexander, Bartholomew, Abraham, Tobias, and Roger, infant children of the aforesaid, were also dead and buried; and that the dark flat wilderness beyond the churchyard, intersected with dykes and mounds and gates, with scattered cattle feeding on it, was the marshes; and that the low leaden line beyond was the river; and that the distant savage lair from which the wind was rushing, was the sea; and that the small bundle of shivers growing afraid of it all and beginning to cry, was Pip.

Illustration by F. W. Pailthorpe.

Wackford Squeers

Nicholas Nickleby, Chapter 4

Wackford Squeers is the most violent and rapacious of Dickens' evil schoolmasters.

Mr. Squeers's appearance was not prepossessing. He had but one eye, and the popular prejudice runs in favour of two. The eye he had, was unquestionably useful, but decidedly not ornamental: being of a greenish grey, and in shape resembling the fan-light of a street door. The blank side of his face was much wrinkled and puckered up, which gave him a very sinister appearance, especially when he smiled, at which times his expression bordered closely on the villanous. His hair was very flat and shiny, save at the ends, where it was brushed stiffly up from a low protruding forehead, which assorted well with his harsh voice and coarse manner. He was about two or three and fifty, and a trifle below the middle size; he wore a white neckerchief with long ends, and a suit of scholastic black; but his coat sleeves being a great deal too long, and his trousers a great deal too short, he appeared ill at ease in his clothes, and as if he were in a perpetual state of astonishment at finding himself so respectable.

Mr. Squeers was standing in a box by one of the coffee-room fire-places, fitted with one such table as is usually seen in coffee-rooms, and two of extraordinary shapes and dimensions made to suit the angles of the partition. In a corner of the seat, was a very small deal trunk, tied round with a scanty piece of cord; and on the trunk was perched–his lace-up half-boots and corduroy trousers dangling in the air–a diminutive boy, with his shoulders drawn up to his ears, and his hands planted on his knees, who glanced timidly at the schoolmaster, from time to time, with evident dread and apprehension.

"Half-past three," muttered Mr. Squeers, turning from the window, and looking sulkily at the coffee-room clock. "There will be nobody here to-day."

Much vexed by this reflection, Mr. Squeers looked at the little boy to see whether he was doing anything he could beat him for. As he happened not to be doing anything at all, he merely boxed his ears, and told him not to do it again.

"At Midsummer," muttered Mr. Squeers, resuming his complaint, "I took down ten boys; ten twentys is two hundred pound. I go back at eight o'clock to-morrow morning, and have got only three–three oughts is an ought–three twos is six–sixty pound. What's come of all the boys? what's parents got in their heads? what does it all mean?"

Wackford Squeers attending to his pupils in *Nicholas Nickleby.*

Wackford Squeers Boarding School

Nicholas Nickleby, Chapter 7, Chapter 8

Called Dotheboys Hall, this is the location of Nicholas's first job. These scenes were based on Dickens' own observations, which led to government investigation and reform of such "schools."

Is it much farther to Dotheboys Hall, sir?" asked Nicholas.

"About three mile from here," replied Squeers. "But you needn't call it a Hall down here."

Nicholas coughed, as if he would like to know why.

"The fact is, it ain't a Hall," observed Squeers drily.

"Oh, indeed!" said Nicholas, whom this piece of intelligence much astonished.

"No," replied Squeers. "We call it a Hall up in London, because it sounds better, but they don't know it by that name in these parts. A man may call his house an island if he likes; there's no act of Parliament against that, I believe?"

"I believe not, sir," rejoined Nicholas.

Squeers eyed his companion slily, at the conclusion of this little dialogue, and finding that he had grown thoughtful and appeared in nowise disposed to volunteer any observations, contented himself with lashing the pony until they reached their journey's end.

* * *

Now, the fact was, that both Mr. and Mrs. Squeers viewed the boys in the light of their proper and natural enemies; or, in other words, they held and considered that their business and profession was to get as much from every boy as could by possibility be screwed out of him. On this point they were both agreed, and behaved in unison accordingly. The only difference between them was, that Mrs. Squeers waged war against the enemy openly and fearlessly, and that Squeers covered his rascality, even at home, with a spice of his habitual deceit; as if he really had a notion of some day or other being able to take himself in, and persuade his own mind that he was a very good fellow.

"But come," said Squeers, interrupting the progress of some thoughts to this effect in the mind of his usher, "let's go to the school-room; and lend me a hand with my school coat, will you?"

Nicholas assisted his master to put on an old fustian shooting-jacket, which he took down from a peg in the passage; and Squeers, arming himself with his cane, led the way across a yard, to a door in the rear of the house.

"There," said the schoolmaster as they stepped in together; "this is our shop, Nickleby!"

It was such a crowded scene, and there were so many objects to attract attention, that, at first, Nicholas stared about him, really without seeing anything at all. By degrees, however, the place resolved itself into a bare and dirty room, with a couple of windows, whereof a tenth part might be of glass, the remainder being stopped up with old copybooks and paper. There were a couple of long old rickety desks, cut and notched, and inked, and damaged, in every possible way; two or three forms; a detached desk for Squeers; and another for his assistant. The ceiling was supported, like that of a barn, by cross beams and rafters; and the walls were so stained and discoloured, that it was impossible to tell whether they had ever been touched with paint or whitewash.

But the pupils–the young noblemen! How the last faint traces of hope, the remotest glimmering of any good to be derived from his efforts in this den, faded from the mind of Nicholas as he looked in dismay around! Pale and haggard faces, lank and bony figures, children with the countenances of old men, deformities with irons upon their limbs, boys of stunted growth, and others whose long meagre legs would hardly bear their stooping bodies, all crowded on the view together; there were the bleared eye, the hare-lip, the crooked foot, and every ugliness or distortion that told of unnatural aversion conceived by parents for their offspring, or of young lives which, from the earliest dawn of infancy, had been one horrible endurance of cruelty and neglect. There were little faces which should have been handsome, darkened with the scowl of sullen, dogged suffering; there was childhood with the light of its eye quenched, its beauty gone, and its helplessness alone remaining; there were vicious-faced boys, brooding, with leaden eyes, like malefactors in a jail; and there were young creatures on whom the sins of their frail parents had descended, weeping even for the mercenary nurses they had known, and lonesome even in their loneliness. With every kindly sympathy and affection blasted in its birth, with every young and healthy feeling flogged and starved down, with every revengeful passion that can fester in swollen hearts, eating its evil way to their core in silence, what an incipient Hell was breeding here!

Walpole Tailors

David Copperfield, Chapter 9

Although there are other tailors in Dickens, Mr. Omer is a kindly man, and the best representative of his profession. Here is a touching scene, where young David is measured for mourning clothes, while the coffin of his mother is hammered together.

I left Salem House upon the morrow afternoon. I little thought then that I left it, never to return. We travelled very slowly all night, and did not get into Yarmouth before nine or ten o'clock in the morning. I looked out for Mr. Barkis, but he was not there; and instead of him a fat, shortwinded, merry-looking, little old man in black, with rusty little bunches of ribbons at the knees of his breeches, black stockings, and a broad-brimmed hat, came puffing up to the coach-window, and said:

"Master Copperfield?"

"Yes, sir."

"Will you come with me, young sir, if you please," he said, opening the door, "and I shall have the pleasure of taking you home."

I put my hand in his, wondering who he was, and we walked away to a shop in a narrow street, on which was written Omer, Draper, Tailor, Haberdasher, Funeral Furnisher, &c. It was a close and stifling little shop; full of all sorts of clothing, made and unmade, including one window full of beaver-hats and bonnets. We went into a little back-parlor behind the shop, where we found three young women at work on a quantity of black materials, which were heaped upon the table, and little bits and cuttings of which were littered all over the floor. There was a good fire in the room, and a breathless smell of warm black crape–I did not know what the smell was then, but I know now.

The three young women, who appeared to be very industrious and comfortable, raised their heads to look at me, and then went on with their work. Stitch, stitch, stitch. At the same time there came from a workshop across a little yard outside the window, a regular sound of hammering that kept a kind of tune: RAT-tat-tat, RAT-tat-tat, RAT-tat-tat, without any variation.

"Well!" said my conductor to one of the three young women. "How do you get on, Minnie?"

"We shall be ready by the trying-on time," she replied gaily, without looking up. "Don't you be afraid, father."

Mr. Omer took off his broad-brimmed hat, and sat down and panted. He was so fat that he was obliged to pant some time before he could say:

"That's right."

"Father!" said Minnie, playfully. "What a porpoise you do grow !"

"Well, I don't know how it is, my dear," he replied, considering about it. "I *am* rather so."

"You are such a comfortable man, you see," said Minnie. "You take things so easy."

"No use taking 'em otherwise, my dear," said Mr. Omer.

"No, indeed," returned his daughter. "We are all pretty gay here, thank Heaven! Ain't we, father?"

"I hope so, my dear," said Mr. Omer. "As I have got my breath now, I think I'll measure this young scholar. Would you walk into the shop, Master Copperfield?"

I preceded Mr. Omer, in compliance with his request; and after showing me a roll of cloth which he said was extra super, and too good mourning for anything short of parents, he took my various dimensions, and put them down in a book. While he was recording them he called my attention to his stock in trade, and to certain fashions which he said had "just come up," and to certain other fashions which he said had "just gone out."

"And by that sort of thing we very often lose a little mint of money," said Mr. Omer. "But fashions are like human beings. They come in, nobody knows when, why, or how; and they go out, nobody knows when, why, or how. Everything is like life, in my opinion, if you look at it in that point of view."

I was too sorrowful to discuss the question, which would possibly have been beyond me under any circumstances; and Mr. Omer took me back into the parlor, breathing with some difficulty on the way.

He then called down a little break-neck range of steps behind a door: "Bring up that tea and bread-and-butter!" which, after some time, during which

I sat looking about me and thinking, and listening to the stitching in the room and the tune that was being hammered across the yard, appeared on a tray, and turned out to be for me.

"I have been acquainted with you," said Mr. Omer, after watching me for some minutes, during which I had not made much impression on the breakfast, for the black things destroyed my appetite, "I have been acquainted with you a long time, my young friend."

"Have you, sir?"

"All your life," said Mr. Omer. "I may say before it. I knew your father before you. He was five foot nine and a half, and he lays in five and twenty foot of ground."

"RAT-tat-tat, RAT-tat-tat, RAT-tat-tat," across the yard.

"He lays in five and twenty foot of ground, if he lays in a fraction," said Mr. Omer, pleasantly. "It was either his request or her direction, I forget which."

"Do you know how my little brother is, sir?" I enquired.

Mr. Omer shook his head.

"RAT-tat-tat, RAT-tat-tat, RAT-tat-tat."

"He is in his mother's arms," said he.

"Oh, poor little fellow! Is he dead?"

"Don't mind it more than you can help," said Mr. Omer. "Yes. The baby's dead."

My wounds broke out afresh at this intelligence. I left the scarcely-tasted breakfast, and went and rested my head on another table in a corner of the little room, which Minnie hastily cleared, lest I should spot the mourning that was lying there with my tears. She was a pretty good-natured girl, and put my hair away from my eyes with a soft kind touch; but she was very cheerful at having nearly finished her work and being in good time, and was so different from me!

C.H. Watt Physician (Residence)

Pickwick Papers, Chapter 44

Sam Weller tells the story with a surprise ending of the principled patient and the imperious doctor.

I takes my determination on principle, sir," remarked Sam, "and you takes yours on the same ground; wich puts me in mind o' the man as killed his-self on principle, wich o' course, you've heerd on, sir." Mr. Weller paused when he arrived at this point, and cast a comical look at his master out of the corners of his eyes.

"There is no 'of course' in the case, Sam," said Mr. Pickwick, gradually breaking into a smile, in spite of the uneasiness which Sam's obstinacy had given him. "The fame of the gentleman in question, never reached my ears."

"No, sir!" exclaimed Mr. Weller. "You astonish me, sir; he wos a clerk in a gov'ment office, sir."

"Was he?" said Mr. Pickwick.

"Yes, he wos, sir," rejoined Mr. Weller; "and a wery pleasant gen'l'm'n too–one o' the precise and tidy sort, as puts their feet in little India-rubber fire-buckets wen it's wet weather, and never has no other bosom friends but hare-skins; he saved up his money on principle, wore a clean shirt ev'ry day on principle; never spoke to none of his relations on principle, 'fear they shou'd want to borrow money of him; and wos altogether, in fact, an uncommon agreeable character. He had his hair cut on principle vunce a fortnight, and contracted for his clothes on the economic principle–three suits a year, and send back the old uns. Being a wery reg'lar gen'l'm'n, he din'd ev'ry day at the same place, where it wos one and nine to cut off the joint, and a wery good one and nine's worth he used to cut, as the landlord often said, with the tears a tricklin' down his face: let alone the way he used to poke the fire in the vinter time, which wos a dead loss o' four-pence ha'penny a day: to say nothin' at all o' the aggrawation o' seein' him do it. So uncommon grand with it too! 'Post arter the next gen'l'm'n,' he sings out ev'ry day ven he comes in. 'See arter the Times, Thomas; let me look at the Mornin' Herald, wen it's out o' hand; don't forget to bespeak the Chronicle; and just bring the 'Tizer, vill you:' and then he'd set vith his eyes fixed on the clock, and rush out, just a quarter of a minit afore the time, to waylay the boy as wos a comin' in with the evenin' paper, wich he'd read with sich intense interest and persewerance as worked the other customers up to the wery confines o' desperation and insanity, 'specially one i-rascible old gen'l'm'n as the vaiter wos always obliged to keep a sharp eye on, at sich times, fear he should be tempted to commit some rash act with the carving knife. Vell, sir, here he'd stop, occupyin' the best place for three hours, and never takin' nothin' arter his dinner, but sleep, and then he'd go away to a coffee-house a few streets off, and have a small pot o' coffee and four crumpets, arter wich he'd walk home to Kensington and go to bed. One night he wos took very ill; sends for a doctor; doctor comes in a green fly, with a kind o' Robinson Crusoe set o' steps, as he could let down wen he got out, and pull up arter him wen he got in, to perwent the necessity o' the coachman's gettin' down, and thereby undeceivin' the public by lettin' 'em see that it wos only a livery coat as he'd got on, and not the trousers to match. 'Wot's the matter?' says the doctor. 'Wery ill,' says the patient. 'Wot have you been a eatin' on?' says the doctor. 'Roast weal,' says the patient. 'Wot's the last thing you dewoured?' says the doctor. 'Crumpets,' says the patient. 'That's it!' says the doctor. 'I'll send you a box of pills directly, and don't you never take no more of 'em,' he says. 'No more o' wot?' says the patient–'Pills?' 'No; crumpets,' says the doctor. 'Wy?' says the patient, starting up in bed; 'I've eat four crumpets, ev'ry night for fifteen year, on principle.' 'Well, then, you'd better leave 'em off, on principle,' says the doctor. 'Crumpets is wholesome, sir,' says the patient. 'Crumpets is not wholesome, sir,' says the doctor, wery fierce. 'But they're so cheap,' says the patient, comin' down a little, 'and so wery fillin' at the price.' 'They'd be dear to you, at any price; dear if you wos paid to eat 'em,' says the doctor. 'Four crumpets a night,' he says, 'vill do your business in six months!' The patient looks him full in the face, and turns it over in his mind for a long time, and at last he says, 'Are you sure o' that 'ere, sir?' 'I'll stake my professional reputation on it,' says the doctor. 'How many crumpets, at a sittin', do you think 'ud kill me off at once?' says the patient. 'I don't know,' says the doctor. 'Do you think half a crown's wurth 'ud do it?' says the patient. 'I think it might,' says the doctor. 'Three shillins' wurth 'ud be sure to do it, I s'pose?' says the patient. 'Certainly,' says the doctor. 'Wery good,' says the patient; 'good night.' Next mornin' he gets up, has a fire lit, orders in three shillins' wurth o' crumpets, toasts 'em all, eats 'em all, and blows his brains out."

"What did he do that for?" inquired Mr. Pickwick abruptly; for he was considerably startled by this tragical termination of the narrative.

"Wot did he do it for, sir?" reiterated Sam. "Wy, in support of his great principle that crumpets wos wholesome, and to show that he wouldn't be put out of his way for nobody!"

Geo. Weeton Watchmaker

Martin Chuzzlewit, Chapter 5

A *street of shops is seen through the eyes of Mr. Pinch.*

But the shops. First of all, there were the jewellers' shops, with all the treasures of the earth displayed therein, and such large silver watches hanging up in every pane of glass, that if they were anything but first-rate goers it certainly was not because the works could decently complain of want of room. In good sooth they were big enough, and perhaps, as the saying is, ugly enough, to be the most correct of all mechanical performers; in Mr. Pinch's eyes, however, they were smaller than Geneva ware; and when he saw one very bloated watch announced as a repeater, gifted with the uncommon power of striking every quarter of an hour inside the pocket of its happy owner, he almost wished that he were rich enough to buy it.

But what were even gold and silver, precious stones and clockwork, to the bookshops, whence a pleasant smell of paper freshly pressed came issuing forth, awakening instant recollections of some new grammar had at school, long time ago, with 'Master Pinch, Grove House Academy,' inscribed in faultless writing on the fly-leaf! That whiff of russia leather, too, and all those rows on rows of volumes, neatly ranged within: what happiness did they suggest! And in the window were the spick-and-span new works from London, with the title-pages, and sometimes even the first page of the first chapter, laid wide open: tempting unwary men to begin to read the book, and then, in the impossibility of turning over, to rush blindly in, and buy it! Here too were the dainty frontispiece and trim vignette, pointing like hand-posts on the outskirts of great cities, to the rich stock of incident beyond; and store of books, with many a grave portrait and time-honoured name, whose matter he knew well, and would have given mines to have, in any form, upon the narrow shelf beside his bed at Mr. Pecksniff's. What a heart-breaking shop it was!

There was another; not quite so bad at first, but still a trying shop; where children's books were sold, and where poor Robinson Crusoe stood alone in his might, with dog and hatchet, goat-skin cap and fowling-pieces; calmly surveying Philip Quarll and the host of imitators round him, and calling Mr. Pinch to witness that he, of all the crowd, impressed one solitary foot-print on the shore of boyish memory, whereof the tread of generations should not stir the lightest grain of sand. And there too were the Persian tales, with flying chests and students of enchanted books shut up for years in caverns: and there too was Abudah, the merchant, with the terrible little old woman hobbling out of the box in his bedroom: and there the mighty talisman, the rare Arabian Nights, with Cassim Baba, divided by four, like the ghost of a dreadful sum, hanging up, all gory, in the robbers' cave. Which matchless wonders, coming fast on Mr. Pinch's mind, did so rub up and chafe that wonderful lamp within him, that when he turned his face towards the busy street, a crowd of phantoms waited on his pleasure, and he lived again, with new delight, the happy days before the Pecksniff era.

He had less interest now in the chemists' shops, with their great glowing bottles (with smaller repositories of brightness in their very stoppers); and in their agreeable compromises between medicine and perfumery, in the shape of tooth-some lozenges and virgin honey. Neither had he the least regard (but he never had much) for the tailors', where the newest metropolitan waistcoat patterns were hanging up, which by some strange transformation always looked amazing there, and never appeared at all like the same thing anywhere else. But he stopped to read the playbill at the theatre, and surveyed doorway with a kind of awe, which was not diminished when a sallow gentleman with long dark hair came out, and told a boy to run home to his lodgings and bring down his broadsword.

Mr. Pinch stood rooted to the spot on hearing this, and might have stood there until dark, but that the old cathedral bell began to ring for vesper service, on which he tore himself away.

Mr. Wickfield Solicitor (and Tudor Cottage)

David Copperfield , Chapter 15

Not only is David's beloved home away from home described, but here he meets his enemy Uriah Heep, and his only true friend, Agnes Wickfield. Aunt Betsey always calls David "Trotwood."

My aunt, who was perfectly indifferent to public opinion, drove the grey pony through Dover in a masterly manner; sitting high and stiff like a state coachman, keeping a steady eye upon him wherever he went, and making a point of not letting him have his own way in any respect. When we came into the country road, she permitted him to relax a little, however; and looking at me down in a valley of cushion by her side, asked me whether I was happy?

"Very happy indeed, thank you, aunt," I said.

She was much gratified; and both her hands being occupied, patted me on the head with her whip.

"Is it a large school, aunt ?" I asked.

"Why, I don't know," said my aunt. "We are going to Mr. Wickfield's first."

"Does *he* keep a school?" I asked.

"No, Trot," said my aunt. "He keeps an office."

I asked for no more information about Mr. Wickfield, as she offered none, and we conversed on other subjects until we came to Canterbury, where, as it was market-day, my aunt had a great opportunity of insinuating the grey pony among carts, baskets, vegetables, and hucksters' goods. The hair-breadth turns and twists we made, drew down upon us a variety of speeches from the people standing about, which were not always complimentary; but my aunt drove on with perfect indifference, and I dare say would have taken her own way with as much coolness through an enemy's country.

At length we stopped before a very old house bulging out over the road;

a house with long low lattice-windows bulging out still farther, and beams with carved heads on the ends bulging out too, so that I fancied the whole house was leaning forward, trying to see who was passing on the narrow pavement below. It was quite spotless in its cleanliness. The old-fashioned brass knocker on the low arched door, ornamented with carved garlands of fruit and flowers, twinkled like a star; the two stone steps descending to the door were as white as if they had been covered with fair linen; and all the angles and corners, and carvings and mouldings, and quaint little panes of glass, and quainter little windows, though as old as the hills, were as pure as any snow that ever fell upon the hills.

When the pony-chaise stopped at the door, and my eyes were intent upon the house, I saw a cadaverous face appear at a small window on the groundfloor (in a little round tower that formed one side of the house), and quickly disappear. The low arched door then opened, and the face came out. It was quite as cadaverous as it had looked in the window, though in the grain of it there was that tinge of red which is sometimes to be observed in the skins of red-haired people. It belonged to a red-haired person–a youth of fifteen, as I take it now, but looking much older–whose hair was cropped as close as the closest stubble; who had hardly any eyebrows, and no eyelashes, and eyes of a red-brown, so unsheltered and unshaded, that I remember wondering how he went to sleep. He was high-shouldered and bony; dressed in decent black, with a white wisp of a neckcloth; buttoned up to the throat; and had a long, lank, skeleton hand, which particularly attracted my attention, as he stood at the pony's head, rubbing his chin with it, and looking up at us in the chaise.

"Is Mr. Wickfield at home, Uriah Heep ?" said my aunt.

"Mr. Wickfield's at home, ma'am," said Uriah Heep, "if you'll please to walk in there:"–pointing with his long hand to the room he meant.

We got out; and leaving him to hold the pony, went into a long low parlor looking towards the street, from the window of which I caught a glimpse, as I went in, of Uriah Heep breathing into the pony's nostrils, and immediately covering them with his hand, as if he were putting some spell upon him. Opposite to the tall old chimney-piece, were two portraits: one of a gentleman with grey hair (though not by any means an old man) and black eyebrows, who was looking over some papers tied together with red tape; the other, of a lady, with a very placid and sweet expression of face, who was looking at me.

I believe I was turning about in search of Uriah's picture, when, a door at the farther end of the room opening, a gentleman entered, at sight of whom I turned to the first-mentioned portrait again, to make quite sure that it had not come out of its frame. But it was stationary; and as the gentleman advanced into the light, I saw that he was some years older than when he had had his picture painted.

About the Illustrations

The many illustrations in this book which are unattributed are the work of one man, known as "Phiz," whose name was Hablôt K. Browne. These drawings are the original illustrations which accompanied each month's installment of the serial novel. Browne and Dickens met when they were both young and just beginning their careers. Dickens' first important job was to write monthly text to accompany the humorous drawings of a popular artist, Robert Seymour. The book was *The Posthumous Papers of the Pickwick Club.* Seymour committed suicide after only making a few drawings; the drawings by an artist commissioned by the publisher were unacceptable. When Browne submitted drawings for Dickens' consideration, and Dickens accepted, they began a collaboration that lasted for twenty-three years. Eventually Browne drew and engraved hundreds of drawings for Dickens' books.

Dickens worked very closely with Browne and his other illustrators, correcting tiny details, and sometimes being quite demanding. The result is illustrations that are instantly identifiable and exactly as Dickens wanted them to be.

Illustrations from *Oliver Twist* are by George Cruikshank; those from *Great Expectations* by F.W. Pailthorpe. Other illustrations in this book are from various nineteenth-century sources as cited. *The Book of Christmas* is especially interesting because it was one of the first books which recorded a growing interest by early Victorians in the more pagan traditions of the winter holiday. *A Christmas Carol* grew out of this interest, and the popularity of the Carol started traditions which continue unbroken to the present day. Coincidentally, the illustrations in *The Book of Christmas* are by the same Robert Seymour who tragically ended his collaboration with Dickens.

Gad's Hill Place, the last home of Charles Dickens.

If you would like to learn more about Dickens, I suggest that you start with the University of California Dickens Project, where I worked for several years. The Dickens Project provided me nineteenth-century editions of his works to use as my source material, as well as this lovely portrait of Gad's Hill by F. G. Kitton.

The Dickens Project offers programs for scholars, teachers, and the general public. You can write to them for more information about their programs and publications.

The Dickens Project
University of California
Santa Cruz, CA
95064

Linda Rosewood Hooper

1931-HOOP

9 780738 827186 90000>

BVG